# Prader–Willi Sy

# Prader–Willi Syndrome

## Home, school and community

*Terrance N. James*
District Vice Principal,
Special Education Services, Courtenay, Canada

and

*Roy I. Brown*
Professor of Educational Psychology and
Director of Rehabilitation Studies,
University of Calgary, Canada

**CHAPMAN & HALL**
London · New York · Tokyo · Melbourne · Madras

**Published by Chapman & Hall, 2–6 Boundary Row, London SE1 8HN**

---

Chapman & Hall, 2–6 Boundary Row, London SE1 8HN, UK

Chapman & Hall, 29 West 35th Street, New York NY10001, USA

Chapman & Hall Japan, Thomson Publishing Japan, Hirakawacho Nemoto Building, 7F, 1-7-11 Hirakawa-cho, Chiyoda-ku, Tokyo 102, Japan

Chapman & Hall Australia, Thomas Nelson Australia, 102 Dodds Street, South Melbourne, Victoria 3205, Australia

Chapman & Hall India, R. Seshadri, 32 Second Main Road, CIT East, Madras 600 035, India

---

Distributed in the USA and Canada by Singular Publishing Group, Inc.,
4284 41st Street, San Diego, California 92105

First edition 1992


Typeset in Linotron Palatino by Intype, London
Printed in Great Britain by St Edmundsbury Press Ltd, Bury St Edmunds, Suffolk

ISBN 0 412 45360 6 156593 046 0 (USA)



A catalogue record for this book is available from the British Library

This book is dedicated to those individuals with Prader–Willi syndrome, and their families, throughout western Canada, who have contributed so generously in the interest of research and helping others.

# Contents

# Preface

During doctoral research undertaken into psycho-social aspects of Prader–Willi syndrome (PWS) it became apparent that there was a great need for information from social, psychological, and educational perspectives to support parents and non-medical professionals working with the syndrome on a day-to-day basis. The expressed need of many concerned individuals became the impetus for this text. While medical practitioners will find the material helpful, particularly from the standpoint of prognostic information, no attempt is made to explore the biomedical aspects of the disorder beyond those that are necessary to present the syndrome in context. Parents, social services professionals, and students of rehabilitation education, on the other hand, will find the book of considerable interest. As far as we know, it represents the first attempt to address specifically the psychological, social, and educational aspects of PWS in a text format.

The data which form the basis for much of the discussion was gathered in a survey study undertaken during 1986. The research was conducted through in-home visits to families with Prader–Willi syndrome dependants in the four western provinces of Canada, covering a geographic distance of some 2 500 kilometres. The naturalistic approach allowed for participant observation in home and school environments, and provided a rich source of qualitative information in addition to quantitative data collection. Casework conducted by the authors in clinical and community settings provides additional illustrative examples throughout. All case examples are Canadian, and represent a new contribution to the PWS literature.

While it is not easy to address both a lay and professional audience, effort has been made to provide a balance between technical jargon and everyday language. Short explanations of key terms are given in brackets in the text. For unexplained terms, a glossary appears in Appendix A. Canadian-specific terms that may need clarification are explained in Appendix E. In the interest of lay readability, details of statistical procedures have been omitted; all references to significance should be understood minimally at the 0.05 level.

The original thesis was conducted by Terrance N. James, and supervised by Roy I. Brown within the Rehabilitation Studies Programme, Department of Educational Psychology, University of Calgary, Canada. The authors are grateful to Dr F.D. Oliva for encouragement to put this research into print, and would like to thank Dr J.M. Berg for his helpful editorial comments, particularly those relating to biomedical statements.

# Foreword

Prader–Willi syndrome is a distinctive disorder, though with manifestations of variable frequency and degree, that has been extensively documented since its initial formal description just a few decades ago. Much of the published observations have focused on medical and biological aspects of the condition; however, with increased life expectancy, and the widespread growth in community-based living, psycho-social and educational perspectives concerning Prader–Willi syndrome are deservedly receiving increased attention.

These perspectives are crucial in appreciating and adequately serving the multiple needs of persons with the syndrome and their families. It is entirely appropriate therefore that this book should have a predominantly psycho-social and educational orientation. Though based largely on direct experiences with, and data derived from, over 50 families living in western Canada that have a member with Prader–Willi syndrome, many of the considerations raised apply well beyond those boundaries. The problems facing individuals with the syndrome and their families are not unique, despite social, cultural, and economic differences between, and within, countries; and solutions, though at least partly dependent on local circumstances, frequently lend themselves to application further afield.

The authors are well suited to have undertaken the writing of this volume, both because of their extensive combined professional backgrounds and knowledge, and because they have had a wide-ranging opportunity to interact with affected individuals and their families – and have done so in a manner that clearly recognizes that 'persons with Prader–Willi syndrome are people first'. These salutary circumstances are reflected throughout the book, which provides an instructive account of the nature, nuances, and characteristics of Prader–Willi syndrome and its multiple psycho–socio–educational ramifications. The understanding and analysis of the situations facing these persons, and the considerate outlook towards them results in informative observations and well-founded recommendations throughout. Perhaps most importantly, the emphasis on appropriate interventions and support does much to dissipate erroneous notions, all too frequently heard, of a dismal prognostic outlook. The authors help to redress the balance by indicating that positive outcomes are not only desirable, but also attainable.

As its subtitle suggests, the book fosters partnership between parents and other relatives, and professionals from various disciplines in jointly serving the interests of persons with Prader–Willi syndrome. It is a pleasure to introduce and recommend it to both groups, who between them can significantly enhance the quality of life of those with the syndrome to the benefit of all concerned, and of the communities in which they live.

J.M. Berg MB, BCh, MSC, FRCPsych, FCCMG
Professor Emeritus, Faculty of Medicine
University of Toronto

# Introduction

Prader–Willi syndrome (PWS) is a congenital disorder that was first described by doctors Prader, Labhart, and Willi in 1956. The primary descriptors included: obesity, lack of muscle tone, mental handicap, incomplete sexual development, and small hands and feet. Secondary to the physical and metabolic aspects of this disorder are usually severe behavioural problems, which can have a profound effect on individual and family well-being, and often become a community concern. Since its discovery, a considerable body of scientific literature has evolved, albeit primarily of a medical nature. Beyond health management, there are many problems facing individuals with PWS and their families that demand responses from social science disciplines.

These pages present initial demographic and descriptive data on individuals with PWS and their parents in western Canada. Contemporary issues, centred around home and community interventions, are examined in the light of current research information, and illustrated with case-study descriptions from more than 50 families. It is hoped that this information will help to fill the gap in the day-to-day lay management of PWS in the home and the community.

Chapter 1 begins with an historical overview of PWS and a description of its clinical features. Research is reviewed from the perspective of aetiology (causation) and epidemiology (distribution and characteristics). The chapter concludes with a discussion of the current context of social services delivery in Canada. In order to set the stage, the characters are introduced in Chapter 2. Vignettes of PWS at various stages of development, from the perspective of parents and care-givers, implicating professionals from several disciplines, are provided. Chapter 3 gives an overview of non-medical aspects of PWS drawn from the available English language literature. Western Canadian PWS child and parent characteristics are presented in Chapters 4 and 5. The interventions discussed in Chapter 6 reflect parental perspectives on what is considered to be effective in-home and community management of dependants with PWS. Chapter 7 is concerned with coping within the family, and Chapter 8 discusses coping in the community by examining the environments in which PWS families exist. Chapter 9 addresses emerging quality-of-life issues in the context of current research. Finally, Chapter 10 provides encouragement and an optimistic view for parents and professionals alike. Each chapter ends with a summary of the main points discussed, including recommendations where appropriate. Appendices have been provided for those seeking contacts and more detailed information.

# Chapter 1

# Overview

It is reasonable to assume that PWS occurred before the middle of this century. There is interesting artistic evidence of the possibility of individuals with PWS in the seventeenth-century Spanish court (Steffes *et al.*, 1981; Cassidy, 1984). Paintings by Juan Carreño de Miranda, *c.*1680, of a six-year-old girl called 'La Monstrua' can be found in the Prado. There appears to be no evidence, however, indicating the prevalence of PWS prior to the latter half of the twentieth century. Steffes *et al.* concluded that prior to the work of Prader, Willi, and their colleagues some 35 years ago, adiposogenital dystrophy or Fröhlich's syndrome – characterized by obesity, stunted growth, arrested sexual development, and knock-knees – would have been the most likely diagnosis to be given to persons with PWS. Neither of these diseases, however, involves hyperphagia (over-eating).

During the 1940s, Zellweger (1981) was involved in research on hypotonias (lack of muscle tone, tension, and strength) of supranuclear or cerebral origin in the Children's Hospital at the University of Zurich. Prader and his colleagues followed up many of the same subjects from an endocrinological perspective over a number of years. In 1956 they published the first description of the 'new' syndrome under the title, 'A syndrome of obesity, short stature, cryptorchidism and oligophrenia, with amyotonia in the neonatal period' (Prader *et al.*, 1956). (Cryptorchism refers to a developmental defect whereby the testes do not descend into the scrotum; oligophrenia is another term for mental retardation; amyotonia means a lack of muscle tone.)

In 1965 the term '$H_2O$ syndrome' was used to describe a case of the new syndrome (Holm, 1981a), referring to the hypotonia (lack of muscle tone), hypomentia (lack of mental development), and obesity; an additional 'H' for hypogonadism (lack of sexual development) was later inserted by other researchers (Zellweger and Schneider, 1968). Neither '$H_2O$' nor 'HHHO' syndrome became popular terms, however, and Prader–Labhart–Willi, or Prader–Willi, became commonly used eponyms. Within a decade of the first scientific documentation, case reports of the syndrome were published from England, Canada, the United States, France, Spain, Sweden, the Netherlands, and Belgium (Steffes *et al.*, 1981). Zellweger (1981) pointed out that by 1979 more than 200 cases of PWS had been published internationally; by 1983 more than 400 cases had been described in 159 publications (Bray *et al.*, 1983). According to the American Prader–Willi Syndrome Association, more than 3 000 cases of PWS have now been identified worldwide (Alexander and Hanson, 1988).

## CLINICAL FEATURES

While the clinical features of PWS have been described by numerous authors (Bray *et al.*, 1983; Cassidy, 1984; Hall and Smith, 1972; Holm, 1981a; Stephenson, 1980; Zellweger, 1981), clinicians do not always agree on minimal criteria for diagnosis. Diagnosis is usually based on clinical observation and the natural history, but it is complicated by the range and variability in the features. Age at diagnosis varies considerably: most cases are diagnosed between ages five and ten, when they present as obese children with small genitalia and significant academic and behaviour problems; others are not diagnosed until their second or third decade, when they come to medical attention, often for behavioural, emotional, or psychiatric reasons (Cassidy, 1984). Referral to a genetics or endocrinology clinic is often necessary before a firm diagnosis is made.

Common clinical features according to the time of presentation are listed in Table 1.1. While not every feature need be present for the diagnosis of PWS, some are considered essential in making a firm clinical diagnosis. Generally, these consist of: hypotonia, hypogonadism, obesity, cognitive dysfunction, dysmorphic facial features, and short stature for genetic background (Cassidy, 1984; Holm, 1981a).

The differential diagnosis of infants with neonatal central hypotonia should include PWS, as it is more common than most

**Table 1.1** Characteristic clinical features of PWS

| |
|---|
| *Prenatal* |
| Decreased foetal movement |
| Abnormal position at delivery |
| *Infancy* |
| Hypotonia |
| Feeding problems |
| Failure to thrive |
| Genital hypoplasia/cryptorchidism |
| Mild dysmorphism |
| Delayed motor development |
| *Childhood and adulthood* |
| Obesity/hyperphagia |
| Speech delay/poor articulation |
| Intellectual impairment/school problems |
| Behavioural abnormalities |
| Small hands and feet |
| Strabismus/myopia |
| Skin-picking/decreased pain sensitivity |
| Inability to vomit |
| Scoliosis |
| Mild short stature |
| Abnormal pubertal development/hypogonadism |

*Source*: Cassidy (1984).

other disorders which present with this characteristic (Cassidy, 1984). Differential diagnosis for infantile hypotonia is shown in Table 1.2.

Two distinct phases of PWS development have been documented (Zellweger, 1969; Zellweger and Schneider, 1968). In the first phase, hypotonia, feeding difficulties, and developmental delays in sitting, crawling, walking, and talking are most noticeable. Additionally, there may be an absent or very weak cry. Generally, there are poor reflexes, below-average weight, apathy, small genitalia, and little interest in food. The inability to suck properly and the consequent need for feeding assistance causes an understandable preoccupation with infant thriving during this initial stage.

During the second phase, beginning at about two to four

**Table 1.2** Differential diagnosis of infantile hypotonia in PWS

| |
|---|
| *Cerebral hypotonias* |
| Down's syndrome |
| Zellweger's syndrome |
| Atonic diplegia with cerebral palsy |
| Congenital myotonic dystrophy in infant of affected mother |
| Benign congenital hypotonia (essential hypotonia) |
| *Lower motor unit disorders* |
| Infantile spinal muscular atrophy (Werdnig-Hoffmann) |
| Pompe's disease (glycogen storage disease type II) |
| Benign congenital nonprogressive myopathies (e.g., congenital fibre-type disproportion, central core disease, nemaline myopathy, centronuclear myopathy) |
| Congenital muscular dystrophy |
| Duchenne's muscular dystrophy |
| Myasthenia gravis in infant of affected mother |
| Charcot-Marie-Tooth disease |
| *Spinal cord lesions* |
| Related to birth trauma, especially breech extraction |

*Source*: Cassidy (1984).

years, there is an increased and often difficult-to-control appetite, which if left unchecked leads to obesity. The early hypotonia usually diminishes, although a residual element remains. The short stature, small hands and feet, and lack of sexual development become more apparent. Also, impaired performance and deviant social and emotional behaviours begin to manifest in this phase. Affability in the first phase may give way to stubbornness, hyperactivity, repetitive and incessant chattering, verbal aggressiveness, self-abuse, unpredictable rages, signs of depression, and psychotic episodes (Hall and Smith, 1972; Zellweger, 1984).

The two-phase concept underscores the physical and psychological changes that occur in PWS subjects over time. There appears to be a consensus that the characteristics of the second phase continue throughout life.

Life expectancy is considered to be less than normal. According to Statistics Canada (1990), life expectancy for the average

Canadian male is 73.04 years and for the average Canadian female is 79.73 years. The primary cause of morbidity amongst those with PWS is cor pulmonale (a form of heart failure) related to obesity (Cassidy, 1984). Increased awareness of the syndrome and attention to medical and nutritional management, however, is increasing longevity. There are many individuals with PWS in western Canada approaching their fourth decade; the oldest cases in the literature are females of 65 (Alexander and Greenswag, 1988) and 69 years (Goldman, 1988).

## AETIOLOGY

At the present time, the aetiology, or cause, of PWS is uncertain. While abnormalities of chromosome-15 are evident in 50–70% of cases (Zellweger, 1988), the underlying causation is still the subject of much biomedical research. An ongoing dilemma is whether the inability to detect organic pathology is the result of the inadequacy of the available technology and methods, or whether it truly reflects the absence of such pathology. Refinements in cytogenetic analysis, for example, have increased the likelihood of genetic confirmation in recent years.

### Family recurrence

There have been a number of reports of affected siblings (Clarren and Smith, 1977; Cohen *et al.*, 1973; Endo *et al.*, 1976; Evans, 1969; Jancar, 1971). One study (DeFraites *et al.*, 1975) identified a family with five cases of PWS; another (Lubinsky *et al.*, 1987) described a family with four siblings; yet another (Burke *et al.*, 1987) described three sisters diagnosed in their 20s. Affected identical twins (Brissenden and Levy, 1973; Ikeda *et al.*, 1973) and cousins (Hall and Smith, 1972) also have been documented. Parental consanguinity (blood relationship) occasionally has been noted (Jancar, 1971). Recurrences within families have led to the postulation of an autosomal recessive aetiology (Alexander and Hanson, 1988; DeFraites *et al.*, 1975), however Clarren and Smith (1977) estimated the likelihood of a sibling of a PWS subject having PWS to be 1.4–1.6%. Hence, while genetic factors appear to be important in understanding the aetiology of PWS, the low frequency of familial recurrence, combined with a low prevalence of the syndrome has not provided a large population base for study.

## Chromosome abnormalities

The first report of a chromosomal abnormality in PWS in Canada was in 1961 (Dunn *et al.*, 1961), at the Health Centre for Children in Vancouver, although the patient was not diagnosed as having PWS until later (Dunn, 1968). Early reports generally, however, gave no indication of chromosomal abnormalities. The likelihood of finding chromosomal defects has increased with improved techniques such as those for chromosomal banding.

By 1977, studies (Fracarro *et al.*, 1977; Hawkey and Smithies, 1976) had reported patients with anomalies of chromosome-15. Numerous studies subsequently have reported deletions or translocations involving chromosome-15 (Butler *et al.*, 1986; Cassidy *et al.*, 1984; Charrow *et al.*, 1983; DeFrance *et al.*, 1984; Guanti, 1980; Kousseff, 1980; Mattei *et al.*, 1983; Winsor and Welch, 1983; Zuffardi *et al.*, 1978). Bray *et al.*, (1983) pointed out that it is not unreasonable, with methodological improvements, to anticipate detectable chromosomal abnormalities in clinically diagnosed subjects generally. In a major review of the literature, Butler *et al.* (1986) identified 131 cases which had been examined with high-resolution chromosome procedures, resulting in the identification of a proximal q arm deletion in chromosome-15 in 59% of the cases. In their own clinical and cytogenetic survey of 39 individuals with PWS, a deletion of chromosome-15 was identified in 54% of the cases.

The extent to which submicroscopic aberrations are undetected at present is unknown; it is clear, however, that technical advances in recent years have increased the chances of cytogenetic confirmation of a clinical diagnosis of PWS. Generally, it is acknowledged that there is a recognizable abnormality of chromosome-15 in 50–70% of cases (Zellweger, 1988).

While methodological advances may continue to increase identification of chromosome abnormalities, the underlying causation of PWS is still unknown. Goh *et al.* (1984) reported a patient with an extra satellited chromosome that did not derive from chromosome-15. Considering the variation in reported chromosomal abnormalities in PWS, they suggested that such abnormalities may be a secondary phenomenon rather than the cause of PWS. DeFraites *et al.* (1975) earlier had identified a family with five cases of PWS, and hypothesized autosomal recessive transmission. DeFrance *et al.* (1984) postulated 'a mutant gene with different population frequencies that is suppressed in case of two normal chromosomes 15 present'. Butler *et al.* (1986), however, showed that in 13 families where both sets of parents' chromosomes were apparently normal, 'the chromosome 15 donated by the father was recognized as the chromosome in which the deletion had occurred in the abnormal child.'

More recently, analysis has revealed chromosome deletions in karyotypically normal patients, corroborating the findings that indicated the aberrant chromosome is consistently paternal (Gregory *et al*, 1989). The evidence provided by such researchers, and earlier work by Chamberlin and Magenis (1980), suggests that paternal origin of new chromosome rearrangements is a general phenomenon (Butler *et al.*, 1986). Investigations of the fathers of PWS patients with de novo deletions are recommended by Butler *et al.* as 'male gametogenesis might be more vulnerable to mutations and environmental insult occurring through an effect on DNA replication than female gametogenesis'. Along this line, one recent investigation has found 'a significantly higher incidence of exposure to hydrocarbons at the time of conception among fathers of children with PWS' (Cassidy *et al.*, 1989). These investigators found no differences of significance, however, between fathers of children with and without apparent chromosome deletions. Nevertheless, the high incidence of hydrocarbon exposure suggests this may be a predisposing factor in PWS. The authors indicate, however, that verification of this conclusion will require molecular genetic studies.

## Hypothalamic defect

Researchers have also hypothesized a central nervous system abnormality, probably located in the hypothalamus (part of the midbrain, close to the pituitary), as the causative factor for

PWS aberrations of growth, performance, and various physical characteristics (Clarren and Smith, 1977; Dunn, 1968; Hanson, 1981; Tze *et al.*, 1981; Zellweger and Schneider, 1968). The hypothalamus regulates many vital body functions, such as the neuroendocrine and metabolic activities, temperature regulation, the sleep-wake cycle, and emotional expression. Hence incomplete or defective development of the hypothalamus could account for many of the PWS characteristics. A defect in hypothalamic development might also account for the range of differences observed in PWS by some researchers (Hanson, 1981; Holm, 1981a). The extent and severity of prenatal damage to the hypothalamus could affect the severity of symptom manifestations after birth.

If PWS is the result of a localized defect in central nervous system development, then any factor that could damage that particular region of the nervous system prenatally could be the cause of the pattern of abnormal growth and development (Hanson, 1981). A localized defect hypothesis provides hope for prevention. If environmental factors causing PWS could be identified, then preventive measures may be possible. Evidence in support of the hypothalamic hypothesis, however, is inconclusive. In reviewing available endocrinological data, Tze *et al.* (1981) concluded that endocrine dysfunction is restricted to hypothalamic hypogonadotrophinism, accounting for the hypogonadism, and that other endocrine functions are essentially normal. Further, Bray *et al.* (1983) presented autopsy data on four PWS patients and reported no histologic abnormalities of the hypothalamus.

### Heterogeneous origin

In short, cytogenetic studies to date appear to affirm the possible heterogeneity (different causations) of PWS. The clinical and cytogenetic work of Butler *et al.* (1986) adds weight to the possibility of different types of PWS. On the one hand, there are persons with a chromosome-15 deletion who exhibit the classical PWS manifestations of hypotonia, obesity, hypogonadism, and mental handicap; on the other hand, there are individuals with PWS and apparently normal chromosomes, but displaying classical manifestations. Clinically, however, this latter group appears to be more variable.

Patients have also been evaluated where obesity, voracious appetite, and learning disabilities exist without a clinical diagnosis of PWS. Normal stature and growth rate were observed in five out of six patients between 5–13 years, despite a chromosome-15 deletion (Angulo *et al.*, 1989). Such findings suggest wide variation in clinical characteristics. Suspicions of heterogeneous origin had been raised earlier by several authors (Hall and Smith, 1972; Ledbetter *et al.*, 1981; Zellweger, 1981). If there are indeed a variety of genetic aberrations and/or environmental agents contributing to PWS, a full understanding of aetiology may still be quite distant.

From a psycho-social perspective, there are many questions that may or may not be answered by the above hypotheses. In particular, the presence of mental handicap, specific learning disabilities, and speech and language problems suggest the possibility of more global brain dysfunction or other environmental effects that may be interactive with brain aetiology. Whether future research establishes an underlying biochemical defect or a microstructural abnormality in the brain to explain these and other characteristic symptoms may be an academic issue to lay persons; an understanding of the aetiology, however, might result in environmental, biochemical, or other interventions. A knowledge of the cause of PWS would also be helpful to social scientists and practitioners for family counselling and prevention education. Such understanding is not conclusively available at this point, however, and is not essential for the daily management of persons with PWS.

## EPIDEMIOLOGY

Epidemiology is concerned with the distribution of disease within populations, and characteristics that include incidence – rate of occurrence, such as births; prevalence, or frequency within a population; and racial and sex distribution. Accurate epidemiological information is hard to obtain for PWS due to inconsistencies in data collection methodologies.

## Incidence

Estimates between 1:10 000–1:25 000 place PWS among the more frequently recognized malformation syndromes (Alexander and Hanson, 1988). The estimated incidence of PWS made at the Children's Hospital, Zurich, was about 1:25 000 live births (Zellweger and Soper, 1979). Mascarello (Bray *et al.*, 1983) on the other hand only found an incidence of 1:100 000 in a genetic screening study in California. In Canada, the British Columbia Health Surveillance Registry (B. MacDonald, 1986, pers. comm.; S. H. Uh, 1991, pers. comm.) had too few recorded cases to attempt to compute valid annual incidence rates.

Over the ten-year period 1974–1983, the number of known PWS live births in British Columbia ranged from none to two per year. Hence the live-birth incidence, based on the 1983 birth statistics (Government of Canada, 1985a), could range from approximately 1:43 000 to 1:21 000. For the seven year period 1983–9, however, the rate calculated by the Division of Vital Statistics was 0.02 per 1000 live births, or about 1:50 000 (S. H. Uh, 1991, pers. comm.) Given the difficulties with early diagnosis of PWS, however, incidence figures may not be very useful for comparative purposes. The British Columbia data suggest neonatal diagnosis is becoming more common. In the 1974–1978 period there were only two reported PWS births; in the 1979–1983 period there were six, and from 1984 to 1987 there were five.

## Prevalence

Without systematic data collection procedures, prevalence is also difficult to ascertain. Holm (1981a) suggests that 1:10 000 is a reasonable estimate, based on consultation with North American physicians experienced with PWS. The British Columbia Health Surveillance Registry data had identified 28 cases at year-end 1985. Based on 1985 population estimates (Government of Canada, 1985b) this represents a prevalence of about 1:100 000. Although the Health Registry statistics are more reliable than estimates, as they are based on multiple sources of ascertainment for registrable conditions, the figures must be regarded as minimal ones.

A prevalence survey of PWS in Alberta (Voshart *et al.*, 1983) provides corroborative support for the British Columbia prevalence figures. Voshart *et al.* mailed a survey questionnaire to agencies, schools, and public health units working with special populations throughout Alberta. The 25 PWS cases identified yield a prevalence rate of 1.72 per 10 000 persons under age 34 years in Alberta (95% confidence limits: 1.38–2.06). The 27 cases registered in British Columbia also yield a rate of 1.72 per 10 000 people under 34 years of age (95% confidence limits: 1.07–2.36 cases). The authors concluded that since the population rates for the two provinces overlapped within 95% confidence limits, minimal prevalence figures had been obtained for Alberta. Projecting these figures to include the total provincial populations would result in a prevalence of about 1:100 000 in both provinces. In the absence of other Canadian data, this figure can be considered as a representative, albeit minimal, prevalence rate (James, 1989b).

## Ethnic distribution

Butler *et al.* (1982) noted an apparent paucity of Black people with PWS, and questioned whether this represents a true difference or simply under-reporting. DeFrance *et al.* (1984) found only two such cases out of 300 in the international literature they surveyed, and concluded that ethnic differences seem to be present. Certainly, the early case literature presented mainly Caucasian subjects; however, the early literature was generated from Western countries. More recently, Greenswag (1984a) found Hispanic, Black, and American Indian representation in a North American survey of PWS. The authors are also aware of unreported Canadian cases of oriental and native Indian heritage, and a foreign case of Arabic background. Zellweger (1983) indicated that while the bulk of PWS observations have been from the United States and Canada, there have been reports from almost all European countries, as well as some Latin American countries, Israel, Australia, South Africa, India, and Japan. It is now felt that PWS occurs in all races (Greenswag, 1984a; Zellweger, 1983).

### Sex ratio

Some authors report more PWS males than females. Hoefnagel *et al.* (1967) found males to outnumber females by about three to one in the early literature, which they attributed to earlier recognition of male infantile sexual development. The same explanation was reiterated by Cohen and Gorlin (1969), and by Wannarachue *et al.* (1975). These studies, however, reflect the clinical nature of the early PWS literature. More recent demographic information has led investigators to believe that the frequency of PWS is similar for each sex (Greenswag, 1984a; Zellweger, 1983).

## CURRENT CONTEXT

Any discussion of the psycho-social aspects of PWS must be done in the context of current social policy. Readers who are accustomed to American literature need to recognize there are differences in the application of social policies in Canada. While it is not the intent of this text to make a comparative study in approaches to PWS, attention will be drawn to those areas where Canada exhibits a national distinctiveness. The following contemporary movements notably influence the provision of services and the quality of life for those with PWS in Canada today.

### Normalization

The principle of normalization has had a profound impact on current Canadian social policy with respect to the treatment of people with disabilities. Wolfensberger (1972) defined normalization as the 'utilization of means which are as culturally normative as possible, in order to establish and/or maintain personal behaviours and characteristics which are as culturally normative as possible'.

Normalization has touched the lives of families and changed community attitudes to people with disabilities and the provision of services for them. While the principle is neutral as to whether a specific person or group should be normalized, it is the interpretation and application of governmental policy based on this principle that determines what normalizing measures are offered, imposed, or ignored. As Wolfensberger points out, the principle is deceptively simple, and many human services managers may endorse it while engaging in practices opposed to it. This has been perceived as a problem by some parents advocating for services, particularly when there has been no previous experience with PWS by the agency. Thus, while the principle of normalization has had broad effect, the full understanding of its intent has not been recognized by all human services managers and line staff within provincial social services in Canada.

The importance of normalization can be seen in the Canadian approach to residential services for persons with PWS. While the American approach has been toward the provision of disability-specific, long-term care residential facilities (Thompson *et al.*, 1988), there are few uniquely PWS group facilities in Canada. Instead there is a range of models based on the level of supervision requirements, which is consistent with the desire to provide the most normalized living experiences possible (James and Willott, 1989).

## De-institutionalization

Following from the principle of normalization, provincial governments in Canada have instituted policies to down-size custodial institutions. Some PWS individuals who have been long-term residents of provincial-care facilities consequently have been returned to a life in the community. Even those who had been under custodial care for up to 15 or 20 years have been able to integrate back into the daily life of a neighbourhood. While community living is not without its difficulties, it has given individuals who have undergone the de-institutionalization process a different quality of life and a new dignity.

De-institutionalization is the result of mounting social pressures over the last few decades. Parmenter (1988) points out that the American Civil Rights movement, the emergence of an articulate disabled consumer movement, the growing public awareness of the negative aspects of institutional care, the growth of litigation, and the assumption that community-based care is cheaper than institutional care, have all contributed to the development of present policies. The importance of the need for greater fiscal accountability in particular cannot be over-emphasized. Health, education, and social services, in particular, have been targeted for restraint in recent years. On the positive side, the melding of social and economic concerns bodes well for those committed to the notion of liberating people from institutions, and maintaining them in the community.

### Community living

The independent-living movement has its roots in the desire of physically disabled people to have greater access to the community and hence a more independent lifestyle. At the same time, de-institutionalization was a process initiated to return people with mental handicaps back to the community. The two movements have merged to create new demands in community services for people with disabilities. As a consequence, human services managers at the community level have been required to create resources beyond just residential options. Educational, vocational, and social training opportunities are now available to adults with handicaps in most communities. As Parmenter (1988) suggests, however, often these are the superficial elements of community living that have received the focus of attention. The more critical issues include such things as 'client satisfaction, social and interpersonal relationships, activity patterns, degree of self-determination, socio-economic factors, and access to community services'.

In Canada, the Calgary Association for Independent Living (CAIL) has pioneered an innovative approach to supported independence for community living for persons with complex disabilities, which has involved the concept of individualized service dollars (Marlett, 1988). Funding is customized, that is to say based on individual needs rather than disability categories, and is allocated to people, not programmes or places. One of the early clients was a 26-year-old young woman with PWS. Living in a flat, with a dietary aide, has given her more freedom than living with her parents and being in a behavioural group-home situation. Living with attendant support is one of ten models described in a recent manual on residential options for community living for those with PWS in western Canada (James and Willott, 1989).

The normalization, de-institutionalization, and community-living movements are supported by the Canadian Charter of Rights and Freedoms (Government of Canada, 1984). The Charter recognizes that persons with handicaps often need special kinds of assistance and protection from discrimination, and allows for the establishment of special programmes for persons with disabilities. The spirit of the Charter has resulted in a proactive approach to legislation and policy development in the last few years that has had an impact on all aspects of service delivery. Readers must acknowledge this environment of social change in wrestling with many of the psycho-social implications of PWS contained within the following chapters.

# Chapter 2

# Vignettes

One of the major criticisms by parents of infants or young children newly diagnosed with PWS has been the negative impact of the literature they are given to read. Articles appearing in medical journals are too technical for the lay reader to understand, and often contain clinical pictures of grossly obese, naked clients. Not only is a picture worth a thousand words, it also leaves a lasting mental image that is hard to erase.

The following vignettes are presented early in this text so that readers might identify with the types of issues that parents and helping professionals must deal with on a daily basis. The photo collages have been inserted to provide an impressionistic balance and some visual evidence of normalcy.

While PWS has been described in the previous chapter as a low-incidence medical disorder, the reader should not become preoccupied with the medical nature of the condition while reading this text: it is the social/behavioural aspects of the disorder that demand the constant energies of care-givers and the attention of helping professionals. It is important to acknowledge that persons with PWS are people first – children, brothers and sisters, cousins, grandchildren, school friends, neighbours – afflicted with a medical condition that may or may not prove to be a handicap to them. The photographs have been taken largely by amateurs, to capture memories of family moments and childhood accomplishments. They are in stark contrast to the clinical photographs in many medical journals. While there may be a danger of replacing clinical objectivity with parental subjectivity, from a psycho-social point of view these photographs more adequately reflect the reality of an individual with PWS. The lasting image should be one of joy and optimism: despite the problems presented in this and the remaining chapters of this book, children with PWS are very normal in most respects.

The literature suggests there are key periods when parents of children with disabilities particularly require support: at the time of initial diagnosis, at school entry, at early adolescence, and during the adolescent/adult transition, when vocational planning and residential placement decisions are being made. For most parents of children with special needs these periods are particularly stressful; for parents of children with PWS each period seems to be a prolonged duration of stress, with little differentiation before the next stage begins. It is this intensity that can have such debilitating effects on care-givers, families, and support workers.

The vignettes that follow illustrate some of the typical reactions and concerns experienced by families at stages of development associated with these key periods. Each vignette focuses on a specific PWS concern. All quotations are from transcripts of the recordings made with parents, or excerpts from correspondence received. The names of individuals have been changed to protect personal and family privacy.

## DIAGNOSIS

Diagnosis of PWS does not always occur in infancy. In fact, the average age for the individuals in the authors' files was 3 years 10 months for males, and 10.0 years for females. The discrepancy between these ages is consistent with current literature (see Chapter 4). While there is increasing likelihood of diagnosis in infancy, the authors know of two females over the age of 30, and three more over the age of 25 who were diagnosed within the last few years.

The range in ages at the time of diagnosis results in differing responses and issues. In the vignettes that follow, the parents were responding to questioning about the manner in which they received the PWS diagnosis, and their feelings at the time.

---

**Figure 2.1 on following pages shows typical family photographs of individuals with Prader–Willi syndrome.**

**Manner of diagnosis**

Medical practitioners often have been criticized by parents for the way in which a diagnosis of PWS has been conveyed. A lack of information given, a negative prognosis, an impersonal approach, and a lack of follow-up support can all contribute to a sense of frustration.

> Jennifer was eight and a half years old when diagnosed. I was given the diagnosis over the phone in a rather clinical way and I was in shock. I kind of felt good in knowing that they actually had a name for all these problems that I felt were real for eight and a half years. But when I started reading the literature on it I was really depressed about it. It was really negative.

> Well, I got the diagnosis when he was going on nine and it was kind of an accidental thing. I heard from the dietitian . . . she kind of mentioned the word Prader–Willi syndrome and I said to her, 'I beg your pardon, what did you say?' And she said, 'Dr – said not to tell you this.' I said, 'No, I haven't heard the word before.' So she said that she would check with the doctor. Eventually I spoke with the doctor and he told me about it, but he didn't tell me all that much about it.

> I recall the paediatrician that I had . . . I felt that he was a very negative, non-informative person. He said that she'll never walk, she'll have braces . . . you know, just very sceptical, and a person doesn't really need to hear this. I think it was about age two and a half when she was diagnosed. It was after there was a muscle biopsy to figure out why she wasn't walking . . . I guess I had kind of a mixed-bag feeling, at least I wasn't living in the unknown of making up things about what it could be. But even at that point, there wasn't that much material put into my hands.

> Kim was 12 at the time. A friend had taken a clipping from a 'Dear Abby' column in the local newspaper. The clipping indicated that a boy had died from overeating salt. That was

the story in the column and there was an address of a PW association down in the States that I wrote to. They sent up a synopsis sheet describing the syndrome. When I first read it I didn't believe that it was for real. It was like someone playing a joke. Someone had typed this up, had been watching and typed this up . . .

The one doctor's name was given with the synopsis sheet. That was the only doctor that was listed with the association that I could go to . . . and when I made an appointment to see him he did no other checking except to look at her, to look at Kim and say, 'Yes, your diagnosis is right.' He didn't want chromosome tests. He said clinically she was diagnosed as PW and that was the only thing he offered. There wasn't an ounce of support. He didn't give anything. In fact I would have been better off not to have gone to him because he just caused me a lot of frustration going to him. At the time of the first visit I had asked him if he knew of anyone in the area that he could give my name to. He at that time said he had about 20 patients. Some year and a half down the road I was still asking for my name to be given to any one of them. He really neglected me in that field I think . . . And then finally after a year and a half, at that point I was crying and calling him totally depressed and really down at about once a week I guess . . . About the fourth time in a month that I called him, the last time it was really a bad scene. He finally, over the phone, gave me this man's name.

## Parental feelings

For some parents the diagnosis seems like personal vindication, proof that they had been right in their belief that something has always been wrong. Others feel only personal devastation and fears for the future. Relief is experienced by some, regret by others. Each situation is as different as the personalities of the parents involved.

Fear of what was going to happen in the years to come. And fear of not being able, you know, to be like other kids. Then when we saw, he showed me the book, the fear of him being able to become like that so quickly. The way the book had presented it, there was virtually nothing the parents could do about it in the way of helping or stopping the problem. Since then we have got involved with so many different people and they have shown that it can be just the opposite. The parents have a lot of control over what can happen and it's sad to see some of the parents that don't do anything . . .

Wanda was 16 at the time. My first thought at that time was one of relief because of the diagnosis. Up until this time I was convinced that there was something more wrong than bad temper and needing discipline. I was convinced there was a little more to it than that and the diagnosis finally gave us an answer as to what was wrong . . . everybody seemed to get in on the act at that point. Human Resources had not been involved at all until the diagnosis and then, all of a sudden, they were involved and there were social workers and child-care workers and all sorts of things that I hadn't had before.

The best thing about having the diagnosis was that, as I had mentioned before, now I had a handle on it. Something to tell people if they asked. I had a name. I had a word. I had a category. I had a label. Other than that, I had always known ever since she was born that there was mentally something wrong with her.

Well, I read about it [PWS] first in a newspaper when he was about 15. I guess he was about 16 by the time he was officially diagnosed . . . I remember feeling that I sure would have liked to have known about it a lot sooner, that it could have been helpful for me when he was smaller.

During pregnancy I already had the suspicion that there was something wrong. It was just like a preparation for the birth, I think. It was more complicated, there was more severity than the other two . . . The paediatrician came into the room and she said 'Well, you were right all along. There is something severely wrong with him.' I was devastated; you know, I was very, very upset. What have we done? Why? To accept having a handicapped child I found that very difficult.

Especially having had two beautiful children . . . having a handicapped child there were many questions.

## Support

Once parents have received a diagnosis, there are many questions and emotions that arise. Parents' primary concerns are, 'Why did this happen?', and 'What about the future?' In addition to information, most parents need emotional support: they need to talk about their feelings with someone who understands PWS and the situation. The lack of support has left some parents embittered.

He was four and a half. We received the diagnosis from the Children's Hospital because he had started gaining weight. When he was diagnosed, I was relieved, because up until that point he didn't have a label. So once he received that label for some reason I felt like there was a great weight lifted from me. There weren't very many support systems available. The Children's Hospital were pretty good, like their clinic that they have there, but that was about it. Nobody came out to visit me and say, 'Hey, I've got a PW kid and I know what it's like.' There was none of that.

We were told about her when she was about four or five years old. Our reaction was not too drastic because they didn't tell us too much about it. They told us a few things to expect, but they didn't know very much at the time. So it was just a matter of going along each year and finding out things as we went along . . . We didn't know what to expect. We didn't know what to do or nothing, so we just went along the best we could.

She was five years old when she was diagnosed. I really didn't understand what it really meant when we were told exactly what the problem was . . . They could give me no reason for why it had happened; just that they didn't know themselves.

The concerns expressed above are not unlike those expressed by parents of children with other low-incidence congenital conditions. A full range of parental reaction, from relief to devastation, can occur. All too frequently this is compounded by the manner in which the diagnosis is given and the content that is conveyed. GPs and specialists alike have been criticized by parents for the insensitive manner in which the diagnosis of PWS is given. While some medical doctors may display less sensitivity than desired, however, the majority must be considered to be very supportive. Medical practitioners, it should be noted, express the same frustrations that parents accuse them of causing. Those parents who are critical of the lack of support offered must recognize that there has been relatively little information available to give to parents, other than research-oriented, biomedical descriptions. The need for prognostic information related to non-medical aspects of PWS transcends disciplinary boundaries and parent/professional relationships.

## CHILDHOOD

When a child typically first enters a collective educational activity, such as pre-school or kindergarten (see Appendix E for educational levels for age ranges in the Canadian system), there is generally: decreasing parental supervision, increasing peer influence, greater exposure to the community, more involvement by other professionals, and new demands of an academic nature. For some PWS children second-phase hyperphagia (incessant eating) coincides with the beginning of school, and seems exacerbated by the new environment. The problems that arise at this time generally extend throughout the period of primary schooling (children aged 5–12 years) and are largely of a social/behavioural nature. The following vignettes illustrate the problems associated with the lack of understanding of others, the behavioural concerns that are beginning to emerge, and the supports that are necessary to assist the family at this stage.

## Lack of knowledge and understanding

People cannot be expected to know about PWS – they must be told. It is usually a dilemma, however, about how much to tell. To give too much information might prejudice the treatment of the child; not to give enough might contribute to management problems related to diet or behaviour. In addition, there is the matter of who to tell. Relatives, friends, and teachers usually need to know, although one parent below gives an argument for not telling a teacher. What to tell playmates is often very difficult; knowing something about the playmate's personality and level of understanding is necessary.

> A girl that I used to work with has a child Nicole's age. She's informed her daughter that Nicole has a problem, that she can't eat snacks all the time, that she is slower than her daughter . . . After about the third time she had come over I found her testing. She was constantly asking for food and saying, 'Well, Nicole, you can't have that but I can.' I find she is doing it as a favour to come and play with her but she doesn't really understand. I find that she doesn't realize what she is doing but all this information has been pumped into her and she is playing on it.

> We only have one set of grandparents to deal with and I've given them the literature on it . . . she's read it, but I think she needs more of a definite outline. When Joan goes over there I must say exactly what Joan can have to eat because she is a normal grandmother that likes to feed her things. And so she feels if she feeds her fruit that it's fine, but she gives her a whole apple and a whole banana and bowl of fruit cocktail. . . .

> I see that too often children get labelled. If I was to tell Patricia's teacher that she had PWS, I feel the teacher would go to the library and pick out probably the same medical dictionary that I did when I first found out. And all it says is 'incessant weight-gain' and 'mental retardation' and I don't want her to be labelled that way. She is doing extremely well in school, in her special needs class, and I don't think that

additional information is going to be of much use to her scholastically.

## Behaviour concerns

For the parent of a child with PWS, behaviours relating to food become a major concern. The acquisition of food may be blatant or sneaky. Along with food-access control, parents are also often faced with emerging personality characteristics, such as stubbornness and temper tantrums.

He likes to go downtown and ride in elevators. If we go downtown there is one elevator and it's the elevator he loves going on. He quite often has a little fit over that one. But it's other things, too, that he can't do his own way.

All the children there don't have an eating problem or habit and I find that there's food laying out available for everybody just to help themselves . . . she can't stand watching other children eat . . . She'll stand around and watch and she'll try and sneak . . . whatever is out there. She'll look at me and I have to take her right away from the table. She doesn't throw a tantrum, but she'll be angry with me.

After he was five or six years old he would start eating more. If there was something left on a plate at the table, and even if he was in his high-chair, he would reach across and take it. And of course he started gaining more weight, getting quite heavy. He was quite a heavy little boy. This is what we thought was doing it, the overeating, and then we discovered that this is part of PWS.

He has an awful lot of tantrums and I can't handle him at times. My husband can handle him, but of course he's not here all the time . . . I don't know what to do when he has his tantrums. What do we do with him? I'm afraid he's going to hurt himself . . . We put him in his bedroom and lock the door, but he starts throwing things around, and you know he could break a window or whatever . . . Our latest thing is putting him outside. In the middle of winter-time I've towed him outside. I've actually put him outside and when he starts begging in the window . . . then that's a bad thing too. He could put his fists through the window and cut himself as well . . . The best thing to do is to build a room with some punching equipment . . . where he could go in there and just punch his aggravations out . . . He gets very frustrated with us and he tends to want to kick me and hit me, then he's sorry for it. But at the same time he just can't seem to help himself, he really can't help himself.

We couldn't shop without him, we couldn't visit without him, and a lot of places we couldn't go, we didn't go because he acted up . . . In 1977 we went to a homecoming [football]. He acted up so bad that my husband locked him in the car. He tore the car apart. He tore the upholstery in the car, he chewed the paint all off under the window part in the car. We figured that we'd cool him down, put him in there, but we had to get him out of there . . .

## Supports

For parents fortunate to receive an early diagnosis, some supports such as an infant-development programme, may be available before the school years. It is not usually until the child is part of the public education system, however, that special-education services, including special class placement and/or speech and language therapy, become available. The increasing drain on family energies during this period often requires family oriented interventions, such as respite care, in order to support the PWS child in the home.

Right now at this time I worry about his diet and I worry about his speech. I don't think to the future too much. I don't worry about next year. I just think about today because we never know where anyone of us will be one, five, ten years down the road. So we can't concentrate too much on that especially with a child like him. I just live one day at a time.

She first went to kindergarten (5-year-olds) and enjoyed it. Then when she was six she started at regular school in first grade. She didn't do as well as most children and it was suggested that she repeat this grade. In second grade it seemed to us she had no difficulty in understanding the work but she hesitated about writing answers, then wanted to finish her work when the lesson was over. This attitude about finishing her work in a given time persisted all through her school years. In fact it still does – time to her is not important. In third grade she went into special education. Her vocabulary and her grasp of the subjects was way ahead of most of the other children, but she would not complete an assignment in the time allotted. She spent a lot of time in dreaming, smiling, and talking to herself, or in looking out of the window. She would use any excuse to avoid phys. ed. although she was quite a good walker.

Since we've got this respite care thing it's got a lot better . . . For 16 to 18 hours per week this worker comes and takes her out to various activities. We have a schedule during the week. Tuesday nights she comes and takes her for a couple of hours. They go to T-ball, they go to the pool, they do something. And Friday evening she goes with her. They go to a movie, or go swimming again, or just go to her house and do something. And then she is with her all day Saturday and we have the whole day not to worry about Leona.

It [child-care worker support] started out at 40 hours a week that he was coming . . . Now they pay for 50. For some weeks it can be 52 or 54, it just depends on what is going on. We have had to phone at midnight and he'll come. At 11 o'clock, or 2 o'clock in the morning, he'll come.

Normal childhood development is characterized by increasing exposure to the community. Parents of PWS children often find the demands of educating family, friends, and the community about the syndrome to be onerous. Others' lack of knowledge and understanding, however, can often lead to increased behaviour problems necessitating parental time. From a behavioural perspective, the earlier sound behaviour-management strategies are initiated, the easier the management process will become. Early intervention for behaviour control and weight management will optimize the opportunities for normalcy. Diagnosis at a young age also can facilitate the implementation of community-support services, such as special education, speech therapy, and respite services. Whereas parents of PWS children in the past often have had to manage on their own, younger parents today are more aware of the need for, and willing to accept, the supports available.

## ADOLESCENCE

Adolescence is a confusing time for most youngsters, but more so for those with PWS. At a stage when group identity and subcultural similarities become important, the gap between physical stature, sexual development, mobility, independence, and social activities increases dramatically with peers. As with most of the teenage population, emotional lability also increases during this period.

It must be emphasized that PWS teenagers can experience the full range of emotions and behaviour experienced by their brothers and sisters. Often, however, parents and professionals fail to recognize this. Given the intensity of PWS parenting concerns during adolescence it is not always easy to maintain a clear perspective of adolescent normalcy, and there is a tendency in some families to blame the syndrome for all behaviours. Unfortunately, there are too few professionals available in counselling and psychology with a knowledge of PWS who are able to assist families through the trying times of adolescence. There is a strong need for research to explore psycho-social problems associated with this period. The following vignettes suggest some parental concerns related to adolescent development, some PWS-specific characteristics, and concerns for the future.

### Adolescent development

Three themes commonly associated with normal adolescent development involve sexuality, moodiness, and sibling relations. The following examples, although cited by PWS parents, could easily apply to any teenager.

One thing is her lack of knowledge about sex. She has none at all. She doesn't even know what is happening. She thinks boys are great. They can do anything they want to her, it doesn't matter, as long as they are talking to her.

My major concern with Grant right now is the fact that he is a very moody child. He's very hard to handle at times. It's hard to know how to deal with these things. Another concern that I have is what's going to happen to him in later years. I am concerned about the fact that we may not be able to handle him. It's a stressful situation for us.

It's trying for myself to kind of keep balance between Andrea who is 18, and Sheila who is 11. I think that Andrea at this point is caught up in the fact that Sheila has just shot up and grown exceptionally and Andrea keeps falling back to 'Why am I shrinking?' I can certainly see this from her point of view, but you have to realize that Sheila has her own life too and it's very difficult to try and give always and try to keep that balance and then try to have a little bit left for ourselves.

### PWS characteristics

There are some PWS-specific characteristics that become more apparent during adolescence. While high-pain tolerance may appear at a young age, the increased mobility and independence associated with adolescence increases the likelihood of bodily injury. Scoliosis has been reported in 12%–87% (Holm, 1981a; Laurnen, 1981) of PWS populations studied, and is often not noticed until the teenage years. Behaviour problems usually continue to increase in severity during adolescence.

Robin first began to complain of a tummy-ache on Wednesday evening. She had taken regular meals during the day and had taken part in a 45-minute swim lesson in the morning. She ate only one-half of her supper, but was not running a temperature. She had a normal sleep during the night.

Thursday morning . . . she ate her breakfast and felt well enough to go to her swim lesson. By afternoon she started to have diarrhoea and again talked of a 'tummy-ache', but there was still no temperature. She ate a small dinner, the diarrhoea settled down, and she had a normal sleep on Thursday night.

On Friday morning she felt a little better, again had breakfast and went off to swim class. By afternoon she again complained of a 'tummy-ache' and was very lethargic. She now had a slight temperature, 37.3°C . . . By early evening the temperature had risen to 39°C and I called our paediatrician. From what I described as her symptoms, he concluded that she had a touch of stomach 'flu, but was concerned about the hard abdomen and lack of vomiting . . . I took her to the hospital at 9 pm . . . our doctor ordered blood work and X-rays. The X-ray showed a bowel blockage and her white blood cell count was over 2 000 . . . we decided to start her on an IV, try to insert a gastric tube . . . and monitor all vital signs . . .

Saturday morning brought no change to her condition and the decision to operate was made . . . They found that she had a band of adhesions from bowel surgery at three days of age that was choking the bowel. She also had a Meckels diverticulum and had her appendix removed. She was hooked up to intravenous and gastro-intestinal drainage for five days. All the while she complained very little of pain and by the sixth day was really looking and feeling very well. She remained in hospital for 10 days; returned to school for half days after 12 days, and began another swim class within three weeks of surgery.

The surgeon was astounded by her pain threshold. The severity of the blockage should have had her screaming and writhing in pain . . . she had a 'tummy-ache' and was quite lethargic. He also had never come across a youngster who could not vomit; obviously he had no experience with PWS youngsters. He was also impressed with the speed of her recovery . . .

This was actually our second incident with high pain tolerance for Robin. In grade one, she fell and dislocated her thumb and was crying because of having to miss some school to have her thumb relocated and casted. She would have been happier to stay at school and have her thumb tended to after 3 pm.

Now that we know how her pain tolerance can be, we listen carefully for any complaints and check them out even if they appear minor. We have found that we cannot be too cautious with her and that minor complaints need to be investigated.

. . . eventually I was put in touch with a paediatrician who, I was led to believe, had Prader–Willi as a special interest area. This was all well and good for a number of years, until about three or four years ago, when Andrea developed scoliosis. I sort of felt at that point that, when the situation got somewhat complicated, they sort of passed her along and didn't really want to have any more involvement with her.

They were telling me that she could develop severe behavioural problems. That I wouldn't be able to handle her at home. As a young child she was very, very easy-going and out-going. As soon as she showed any problems at 13, 14, 15, teenage problems I call them now, they really scared me, because I was a single parent. They undermined my confidence in being able to handle her. . . . I think it was exaggerated because I have not had a great deal of difficulty with Krista except when she didn't have a day programme. When she had nothing to do and wasn't able to go to school or anything then we did get into difficulties, because I had to leave her at home alone. I worked part-time myself.

## Concerns for the future

Short-term concern for the future often centres around temporary relief from the burden of constant caring. Respite care is not universally available, but is almost unanimously regarded by parents and professionals as insurance for family stability. Parents look first to their family to assist with the uncertainty of future care. When parents and family cannot cope, they look to residential-care options.

Respite care. As much as we can get of it . . . it's been very good for us. It's the thing that's kept our sanity . . .

> What would happen to him if something happened to me . . . because if something happens to me who knows what would happen, because there is nowhere or nobody who could look after him. I mean, his father could look after him, but he couldn't do it on his own. I know he couldn't. That is my biggest worry . . . I know my sister couldn't look after him. She's been sick too. And there is nobody, absolutely nobody.

> Another concern that I have is what is going to happen to him in later years. I am concerned about the fact that we may not be able to handle him. It's a stressful situation for us and a great concern is a group home for him in years to come.

It must be emphasized again that PWS teenagers can experience most of the problems associated with normal adolescent development. From the point of view of intervention, there is much that can be applied from the fields of psychology, education, and social work to assist with these behavioural concerns. While knowledge of syndrome-specific characteristics will allow for the optimizing of intervention possibilities, adolescence perhaps more than any other stage, requires a plethora of resources. It is the immediacy and intensity of teenage behaviour that causes parents to begin to express concerns for the future.

## ADULTHOOD

The adolescent-to-adult transition is variable in onset and duration. The problems normally associated with transition for many young people are often continuous for those with PWS. There may be ongoing uncertainties with respect to day programming and residential placement that are beyond the control of the family. Ageing parents frequently relate a history of pushing for improved services; the effects of long-term caring upon their own health; and the stress associated with the uncertainty about the future. Specific concerns often cluster around the themes of normalized activity, supports available, and future care.

**Normalized activities**

Parents are most often concerned about meaningful occupational activity and opportunities for independent living. Both of these areas present major difficulties from the viewpoint of the professionals attempting to locate suitable placements. While some high-functioning clients have been under-challenged in sheltered workshop environments, they have at least had reasonable food-access controls; others who have received regular work placements have often failed due to the lack of supervision necessary to monitor them in the community. Independent living is similarly thwarted by a lack of supervision. Normalized occupational and residential opportunities present some of the greatest challenges to parents and professionals alike.

> . . . the work placement. He has been at the sheltered workshop for three years. He has received good training there, I think. But now they have to venture out and eventually have a working place in the community. That hasn't panned out too well. They put him in the food bank for a while. They used it as an incentive. You know, if you get five checkmarks every day for five days a week, then you get to go to the food bank. But then he would leave several times so that was taken away. But that was a great reward to go to the food bank because of the quantities of food and the smells and everything. So I don't think the food bank is a suitable place for him. Neither would be a restaurant. So to find the right working place, a suitable working place in the community somewhere, that is my biggest concern right now.

> My major concern at this time would be for her future living arrangements, for her occupation and type things. I'd like to see her have some more independent living, not living at home. Some sort of part-time job or something that she is committed to other than being home and watching TV all the time.

> I would like her to be somewhere where ordinary kids aren't going to be laughing at her . . . I would like her to develop

to the maximum as much as she can. I just don't want her to be hurt, that's all and I've seen what those kids can do. She is smart enough to know that she is not as smart as she should be. And that's what hurts me the most, knowing that other kids are out there laughing at her . . . This is why I would like, on the one hand, to see her going as far as she can, and on the other hand I would far rather she exist with a tent over her head . . .

## Supports available

The two biggest issues for social services programmes are availability and eligibility. Because many social workers have never had experience of PWS, they must rely on their own interpretation of policy to determine eligibility for services. Consequently, great discrepancies occur in service delivery within and across regions. Feelings of frustration at the lack of supports available, or decisions regarding eligibility for existing programmes may be directed unfairly at social workers. As front-line workers, they too express frustration at the lack of resources and the lack of clarity concerning the application of policy.

They [Ministry of Social Services] say there is no money for extra help, but they say they can take him away from us. For example, we can give him to your neighbour for $1 500-plus, but we can't do it with you.

I find that they [Ministry of Human Resources] are a stumbling-block really. I might add, this is the greatest problem we have encountered in the 22 years of having Sharon.

Sharon went on the GAIN programme through the Ministry and they told me that what to do was have Sharon go to a group home and learn to be independent of her mother. So we went along with that. We didn't agree with it, but we went along with it. It didn't work out and then she was put on a one-to-one basis and as far as I'm concerned it's not working out. I'm told that she is under control and that everything is just fine, but we know she's not . . . She's very depressed and she's not herself . . . She can't seem to brush her hair. She doesn't know when to wash her face now. She

> asked me at meal-time what she should eat first, and she has no initiative of her own . . . She was told that she was one of the handicapped, and this is how they treat their handicapped, and how they deal with them, and we're to go along with it.

> . . . if we don't get some help with her I feel that she will eat herself to death. I'm worried about that aspect, and we're not going to be around always and we would like her – you know, they've had success in the States with these homes, residences. It seems to be the way to go, to be able to control it, and help their behaviours . . . That's what we hope for is something here . . . So far Human Resources have come up with nothing for us.

### Future care

A fair proportion of parents see a PWS-specific group-home as the best option for future care, as suggested in the last vignette. At present, however, there is only one such home known to the authors in Canada. While residential accommodation presents as the immediate concern with respect to future care, there is a broader issue of responsible caring underlying much of what parents express on this topic.

> I think my major concern at this point, I've been talking to many social workers over several extensive meetings, is trying to find a group home that could really work for her . . . that I would feel comfortable having her there . . . that she could have as high functioning as possible, as much independence as possible . . . it all depends on her maturity and what her behavioural consistency level is over the next year and what there is out there. I'm not just going to put her any place.

> Well, the priority right now is a place for her to stay because she can't live at home any length of time; she's too upsetting. And to find, more or less, a home for her. She needs to be in more of a family setting. And I also worry about her on the bus, getting to and from the workshop. And her health, and I often think of the future, and wonder who is going to

> look after her when I'm gone, because my other children are – they're burnt out from her when they were young.

> Well, I had Bobby when I was 39 years old. I'm now 64 and I feel that someday we're not going to be around to look after Bobby. My husband is 65. He [Bobby] should be in a place where they have an understanding of PWS and where, with his co-operation and their help, he can live a fairly normal life.

> It's an awful thing to say, but I have always said that if Jack is going to be institutionalized or going to be knocked from pillar to post like he was before we got him – they said he was in over 50 foster homes – it's not a nice thing to say, but I say that I would sooner see him dead before we go and then I could go in peace and know that he wasn't suffering, not being abused. He has been abused and I know you don't wish anybody dead, but I think he could have a life worse than death if he's to be just left hanging.

At a stage in life when most parents are free from the responsibility of raising children, PWS parents often must continue to provide care and advocate for their dependent adult.

Many older parents have accepted the burden of caring, and only express concern in the light of their own failing health and ultimate inability to continue to function as the primary caregiver or advocate. Despite their personal commitment to the care of their dependant, however, most acknowledge they would not want others to have to face what they have gone through. These parents have been supportive of ongoing research, recognizing that their experiences may be valuable in helping younger families to cope, and in assisting in the design of programmes and services.

## SUMMARY

The vignettes in this chapter underline a number of issues that face parents during different stages of their PWS child's life. While not all parents face the same problems, there is a theme that is consistent with other evidence suggesting that issues relating to development are exacerbated for some persons with PWS syndrome. This includes a heightening of normal difficulties, which is further complicated by some of the features associated with PWS, such as limited intelligence, motor difficulties, and eating problems.

From the above vignettes, it is possible to establish a number of guidelines.

- Medical practitioners and other professionals need to have much better knowledge of the incidence and types of problems and outcomes that occur with children who have PWS. They should also acknowledge the challenges that families are likely to face, as well as the strengths and assets that children may display.
- There must be a greater recognition of the types of support systems required, for example, home relief.
- Because early intervention and improved health-care mean the life expectancy of people with PWS will be longer, considerations associated with retirement of the parents may raise new issues concerning placement of their children.
- Professionals from different disciplines need to work together to lessen the burden for parents. For example, medical practitioners must know something of the resources that can be provided by psychologists, social workers, and educationalists.
- Government social services departments need to recognize the important role they play, and that a rigid interpretation of rules may not bring the necessary services to PWS families.
- During periods of growth, PWS parents may be in great need of assistance. Changing environments from home to school, or children entering new phases of development such as adolescence, adulthood, or reaching the age for employment will precipitate a wide range of new issues in the family.
- Professionals and parents need to recognize there is enormous variability among PWS children in terms of ability, emotional expression, and social development. This makes it very difficult to predict the outcome. The need to provide behavioural support services attuned to the child's or adult's baseline of performance is critical.

- Parents should be given a realistic view of all aspects of their PWS child's life, not just medical.
- Having a disabled child in the family affects all members of the family. The stresses that occur need to be recognized, with steps taken to reduce their sources.
- Although some features are unique to children with PWS, many of their problems are shared with children with other disabilities.
- While there has been an attempt recently to provide as much of a normalized environment as possible for all children with disabilities, for children with PWS there are special issues that must be given greater attention.

# Chapter 3

# Review of non-medical literature

Beyond the health management offered by the medical community, there are many psychological, sociological, and educational problems faced by individuals with PWS and their families. With de-institutionalization and normalization, most older people with PWS have left larger custodial environments and are living in the community. For today's PWS children there are increasing options and supports to ensure integrated community living. There are, of course, problems concerning integration not unlike those faced by other multiply-handicapped populations, but these are exacerbated by the aberrant behaviours and life-threatening implications of food over-consumption. Until recently there have been few published studies by non-medical professionals addressing such concerns. This chapter considers existing PWS research of a non-medical, cross-disciplinary nature.

## COGNITIVE DEVELOPMENT

Most early writers described mental retardation as a primary feature in PWS. Later investigations, however, have shown that mental handicap is a frequent but not consistent feature of PWS (Hall and Smith, 1972). In an American study published in 1981, 12% of subjects were found to be in the normal range of intelligence, and 29% to be in the borderline range (Holm, 1981a). PWS students frequently fall within the borderline or mildly mentally handicapped range, or have learning disabilities (Cassidy, 1984; Lupi, 1988).

A series of experiments investigating the assumption that the causal factors of mental handicap were unimportant in determining cognitive impairment concluded that there are unique cognitive deficits in PWS children (Warren and Hunt, 1981). They have a pattern of cognitive processing different from what a global IQ score alone might predict. Most notably they were found to have difficulty with short-term memory processing and with information-loss from memory over time, yet the speed of memory access to well-known, long-term information was comparable to that of a group of undifferentiated children of equivalent age who were mentally handicapped.

Particularly severe deficits on tasks involving information processing, using the auditory modality, were more recently noted in a psycho-neurological study (Gabel *et al.*, 1986). A description of a girl with a Wechsler Adult Intelligence Scale (WAIS) score of 100, who functions like a person who is mildly mentally handicapped, suggests that subtle cognitive defects that are unmeasurable on standard IQ tests may be present in PWS (Crnic *et al.*, 1980).

It has been pointed out that although many PWS subjects are considered mentally handicapped on the basis of IQ scores, their performance is more like those of individuals with learning disabilities, with considerable variability in relative skills and deficits, and characteristic emotional lability (Sulzbacher *et al.*, 1981).

Holm and Pipes (1976) reported that the intellectual performance of children with PWS declines with age. In a study of 27 PWS children, IQ was reduced both with increasing weight and advancing age (Crnic *et al.*, 1980). Interestingly, a group receiving early intervention to prevent excessive weight-gain maintained a mean IQ score 20 points higher than two obese groups, suggesting that early prevention of excessive weight-gain can reduce the rate of IQ-decline over time. In a recent telephone study of 67 PWS children between the ages of 7 and 11, parental reports indicate higher cognitive levels for children diagnosed early versus those diagnosed late ('The Gathered View', 1990a). Although there is an absence of longitudinal studies, either on single or multiple cases, on cognitive performance in PWS, research to date is encouraging. Early intervention and weight control, when combined with greater understanding of cognitive processes and improvements in special-education methodologies, are likely to enhance the opportunities for cognitive development.

The relationship of cognitive ability to genotype is of recent interest. A comparison by Butler *et al.* (1986) of psychological test performance by chromosome-15 deletion and non-deletion groups found the average IQ for the group without the deletion to be significantly lower than for the group with the deletion. (They qualified their results as tentative pending the study of larger samples with more uniform testing procedures.)

## SPEECH AND LANGUAGE DEVELOPMENT

The effects of PWS may have an impact on a child's communication development. Hypotonic musculature, for example, affects speech production from infancy. With time, the effects of orofacial anomalies and neuromotor impairment may also become apparent in irregular speech production. Zellweger (1988) lists delayed speech as a second-phase characteristic of PWS. Most common speech concerns include problems with articulation, voice quality and usage, and resonance patterns (Munson-Davis, 1988). Although it has been noted that language tends to be a strength in most individuals with PWS (Cassidy, 1984), this is relative to other abilities, and only in comparison with persons with mental handicaps in general. Apraxia of speech (speech difficulty due to a brain lesion) has been reported by Branson (1981) in two PWS children exhibiting severe articulation problems.

As language comprehension is closely related to cognitive ability, it will reflect the range of cognitive abilities of those with PWS. Branson (1981) reported that language skills are more heterogeneous than speech abilities for PWS children and adults.

## SOCIAL DEVELOPMENT

It is the personal-social, rather than medical, aspects that often present the main burdens in PWS (Hermann, 1981), hence it is considered as much a psycho-social disorder as a medical one

(Greenswag, 1984a). PWS children usually fall behind their peers in social-skill development (Neason, 1978). In a survey sent to over 250 families with a PWS child, 58% of the respondents' affected children had moderate or severe difficulties with peer relationships, including lack of friends, absent or decreased play activities with other children, and teasing or being taken advantage of by others (Hermann, 1981). Such problems have been attributed to obesity, behaviour problems, and developmental delays.

Self-concept also is often affected. In the same study it was reported that the ability of 32% of PWS children to like themselves was moderately or severely affected. During the school years there is frequently a cycle of decreasing stimulation, activity, and peer contact that perpetuates isolation. Rejection by peers, with subsequent social isolation, has been attributed to poor peer relations, inability to pick up social cues, immaturity, and the need to be in control of situations (Cassidy, 1984).

Social intervention is best achieved through participation in structured youth activities sponsored by school, church, or community. By the teenage years, however, many recreation programmes are unable to cope with PWS children because of behaviour-management problems, thereby increasing demands on the family to provide their child with appropriate social experiences (Leconte, 1981). Unprecipitated acting-out, mood lability, decreased social-interactive skills, and depression commonly become more pronounced with age, contributing to increased social isolation and poor achievement in academic and vocational settings (W. Mitchell, 1988).

## BEHAVIOUR

PWS children are often friendly, cheerful, and good-natured – but also very stubborn and subject to frequent temper tantrums (Hanson, 1981). The predominant affability of the first phase is often replaced by behaviours that increase parental concern in the second phase. Many parents have reported that even with obesity control and only moderate mental handicap, acting-out and compliance problems often persist, including frequent and unpredictable temper tantrums (Neilsen and Sulzbacher, 1981). Such behaviours become particularly problematic outside the home. The management of PWS child and adolescent behaviours is a primary concern, for example, in the educational setting (James, 1985).

In a summary of clinical experience with PWS, medical investigators described behaviour problems ranging from temper tantrums to rages and psychotic states in at least 8 of 17 subjects over the age of 10 (Dunn *et al.*, 1981). Temper tantrums have been described as 'sudden and short-lived rages, occasionally accompanied by sudden acts of violence' that may occur with little provocation (Cassidy, 1984). In comparing a group of 10 institutionalized PWS patients to a group of non-PWS institutionalized patients, those with PWS were found to be more verbally aggressive, self-assaultive, and regressive (Turner and Ruvalcaba, 1981).

Information on the behaviours of more than 200 PWS adults showed the following common descriptors: slow-moving, good-natured, stubborn, sleepy, belligerent (food-related), irritable, and impulsive (Greenswag, 1984a). Using analyses of variance procedures to compare weight and pondostatural indices (weight in pounds divided by height in inches) with behaviour ratings, the adults with the higher pondostatural indices more frequently were rated as lazy, sleepy, antisocial with their families, and slow-moving. In regard to gender, the only significant difference found was that males more frequently were described as sleepy.

## Food-related problems

Many behavioural concerns are related to food and food acquisition. Gorging, foraging, hoarding of both food and non-food items, stealing money and property were problems cited by dozens of respondents in an adult PWS survey (Greenswag, 1984a). Sneaking food, eating unappetizing foods, and getting up during the night also have been noted frequently (Bray *et al.*, 1983). The insatiable hunger drive found in many PWS individuals has been cited as the cause of frustration, emotional outbursts, and socially inappropriate acts (Greenswag, 1984a).

Educators, perhaps more than other professionals, must contend with PWS behaviours related to food acquisition and consumption. According to James (1985), it is not uncommon for PWS students to eat their lunch before they arrive at school and then lie to staff and students in order to get hand-outs. As teenagers they have been known to barter, borrow, or steal money in order to obtain food. Theft, of course, is the most expedient way to obtain food, and is always a potential problem. Students have been known to scavenge through students' and teachers' desks, lockers, coat-rooms, teacher staff rooms, and other temporarily unsupervised areas, procuring anything edible. Cafeterias, particularly if self-service, are vulnerable to theft as students may consume items before arriving at the till. Vending-machines have been known to malfunction and provide free products; they also can be a source of danger, as when a child has had an arm stuck while trying to reach inside without paying. As James points out, perhaps the most lucrative and consistent source of food in a school setting is the garbage bins. As most educators and custodians know, students are notorious for throwing away good food daily; PWS students can be relentless in their desire to find it.

Holm and Pipes (1976) noted that one peculiar food-related behaviour exhibited by some PWS subjects is the consumption of 'unusual products'. To list the items would give too much credence to a less-common aspect of the disorder, which unfortunately occurs in the popular tabloids. Such sensationalizing of course is damaging by presenting a distorted view of the syndrome.

The social seriousness of the drive to obtain food was exemplified in a recent case in Calgary where the judge fined a young woman with PWS $100 for shoplifting. The woman had taken cookies, chocolates and spaghetti, valued at $4.50 from a drugstore. Despite the request by the defence attorney that the unusual circumstances of the case be considered for a discharge, the judge declared 'You should be treated as others who break the law are treated. You're not permitted to take other people's property' (PWS Newsletter, March, 1991). While the cause of the hunger drive is inconclusive at this point in time, there is general agreement amongst clinicians that there is a physical basis to the problem and that individuals with PWS do not reach satiety. PWS is not an eating disorder caused by emotional or psychological problems.

Reported behavioural interventions almost exclusively are based on single-case or very small group studies. Contingency management procedures have been tried in order to curb inappropriate food-related behaviours. Page *et al.* (1983a) present a two-case study using a token programme based on Differential Reinforcement of Other Behaviours (DRO) to eliminate food theft in a hospital setting. In another institutional study, Marshall *et al.* (1981) give a detailed description of the contingent application of food as a reinforcer to modify food-oriented behaviours, resulting in substantial weight loss.

Both studies, however, fail to show that treatment will continue in uncontrolled settings. Marshall *et al.* conclude that on leaving their programme, 'it is doubtful that treatment effects can be maintained without at least minimal supervision and contingencies'. An interesting contrast to this is the work of Page *et al.* (1983b). Here, a token programme to eliminate food theft, based on simple behaviour management techniques, was expanded to include contingencies for exercise behaviour and weight loss in an institutional setting, and then transferred to a group home setting. Ultimately, the subject moved to a flat where weight loss continued in the absence of structured intervention. Caldwell and Taylor (1986) maintain that the success of their five-week residential programme with 38 PWS individuals over an eight-year period, centred on diet, exercise, and behaviour control training in a normal, open-food environment, suggests that individuals with PWS can 'function in a new or different environments without additional training or without alterations being made to the environment to make it more restrictive'. Recognizing the limitations of externally controlled dieting, Gordon and Clarke-Bruyn (1991) propose that behavioural approaches should focus on the whole personality, not just upon weight and diet control. They argue that individuals with PWS have been stigmatized as being incapable of self-control, and that eating habits and associated behaviours are learned and therefore amenable to the application of learning principles and behaviour management techniques.

## Non-food intervention

There have been few non-food-related behavioural interventions reported. Carlson (1984) described a project utilizing positive reinforcement and group-reward contingencies to reduce maladaptive behaviours in a group home setting. Bahling (1979) commented on the use of contingent non-food reinforcers (phonographs, picture books, story-telling sessions) to increase sitting behaviour and minimize rebellion in one case, and on the use of a student contract with non-food items (picture books, simple puzzle games) as reinforcers at weigh-ins in a programme designed to control physical deterioration in another case. James (1985) described behavioural interventions attempted with teenage students, including attendant care, token economy, contracting, positive reinforcement, group therapy, IEP (individual education plan) participation, deprivation, time out and part-time attendance.

## Psychotherapy

There have been few reports of the use of psychotherapeutic techniques in dealing with PWS-related problems. An encouraging account of group counselling with mildly mentally handicapped young adults in a residential school setting is provided by Goldman (1983). The use of consistent structuring, clear limits, and repeated explanations, along with praise and exclusion where necessary, resulted in diminished social/behavioural problems. Masheim (1981) elaborated on three cases of individual psychotherapy in which anger and aggression were the principal themes. He concluded that 'a significant amount of structuring needed to be done', and that, 'the extent to which the patient allowed the therapist to do this structuring seemed to be one predictor of how much the patient could change in psychotherapy'. He also observed that it was easier to work with patients preoccupied with anger and aggression than with those who were passive-resistant.

A Canadian case-study of a young man with PWS and secondary functional encopresis (withholding of bowel movements) is illustrative of the need for an eclectic approach to treatment. Assessment utilized various developmental perspectives including personality development, cognitive development, physical abilities, sexual development, and stage of family life. Therapeutic modalities included group therapy, play therapy, individual psychotherapy, behavioural therapy, family therapy, and medication (Carpenter, 1989).

In general, behavioural and psychotherapeutic approaches hold some promise for beneficial treatment. At this stage, however, such programmes are still working with single cases or very small numbers. There is a need for larger behavioural studies, particularly of longitudinal design, that would focus on naturalistic rather than clinical and institutional settings. The work of James (1987, 1989a, 1991), centred on home- and community-based intervention strategies, which is important in this respect, is discussed in detail in Chapters 6, 7, and 8.

## FAMILY LIFE

For many families, the presence of a PWS member creates considerable stress. In a survey sent to over 250 such families, only 6% indicated no unusual disruption of normal family living, while 28% reported severe, 40% moderate, and 26% little disruption (Hermann, 1981). In all cases, adaptive changes within the family had occurred before diagnosis was made; the diagnosis, however, helped to establish expectations and also provided parent relief through recognition of a specific problem. In a largely American study (Greenswag, 1984a), diet and weight control, future care, and inappropriate behaviours were identified as the most pressing family concerns with adult PWS members. In a study conducted in western Canada, (James and Willott, 1989), residential-care options were cited as an urgent parent concern.

Most adaptive changes in families relate to food, eating habits, and sibling interactions (Hermann, 1981); in adolescence, social stimulation is also a concern (Greenswag, 1984a). Environmental controls, particularly in the family home, are essential.

The reality of the stress in PWS families has been described as being far greater than that in families of mentally handicapped persons in general (Leconte, 1981), and among parents of

Down's syndrome children in particular (James, 1987). Parents are often exhausted from the demands on their time and energy for specialized programmes, diet control, behavioural supervision, and therapy appointments. Uncertainty and fears about the future are other important stressors.

Parental conflicts may occur as a result of different values in child-rearing practices (Leconte, 1981). To value happiness may mean indulging a child's desire to eat; to value longevity and good health, on the other hand, may require extensive restrictions. The resolution of such parental conflict is important both to parent and child well-being. Unresolved conflicts may result in treatment rejection, or even rejection of the child. Cases of separation or divorce, at least in part related to the presence of a PWS child, have been reported (Hermann, 1981).

Siblings also are affected, experiencing far more intrusion into their lives than is usually the case for siblings of mentally handicapped children generally (Leconte, 1981). Locking up food, restrictive diets, school embarrassment, in-home responsibilities, and disrupted family plans are cited. Siblings may become 'tattle-tales' in order to control the eating of their PWS brother or sister; or harbour 'resentments when their own treats are curtailed or stolen' (L. Mitchell, 1988). According to Tomaseski-Heinemann (1988), siblings also 'fear isolation, worry that the condition is contagious or inherited, wonder if their parents love their disabled sibling more, and occasionally desire to get sick too in order to get attention'. She concludes that the lives of siblings will be 'partly enriched and partly damaged' by the presence of PWS.

## INDEPENDENT LIVING

The prognosis for independent living during adulthood has been poor. A study of 232 North American PWS adults found five to be living by themselves, but weighing 40–50 pounds (18.1 to 22.7 kg) more than those in more restricted settings (Greenswag, 1984a). Those living in group homes weighed the least. The survey found 50% living in their parents' homes; 15.9% in PWS group homes; 15.9% in non-PWS group homes; 8.2% in long-term care facilities; 7.8% in supervised but independent-living settings; and the remaining 2.2% in other situations, for example with relatives. Of the seven Canadian respondents in the survey, three were living at home, two were in a non-PWS group home, one was in a foster home, and one was in a long-term care setting (Greenswag, 1984b).

The American trend is towards the provision of PWS-specific living facilities. Permanent, homogeneous 12–15 bed residences for PWS clients older than 15 years have proved to be cost-effective and programmatically successful (Thompson *et al.*, 1988). Legislation was initiated in California in 1988 to establish the largest PWS-specific residential facility to date, housing 36 clients. With 55 PWS persons in group-living facilities at that time, there were still another 54 on a waiting-list. The Prader–Willi California Foundation (1988) believed that the needs of PWS children could best be served in 'an atypical residential environment', that is to say, exclusively for individuals with PWS.

PWS-specific group-living facilities are rare in Canada at present due to the relatively small population base and the current social policy of de-institutionalization and normalization. A survey of the four western provinces identified 10 residential models within the context of community living (James and Willott, 1989). The models include home living, PWS group home, behavioural group home, group home for persons with mental handicaps, attached suite, boarding home, denominational facilities, independent living with attendant support, independent living with itinerant support, and co-habitation. The case studies illustrating these models suggest strengths and weaknesses of each, with implications for quality-of-life considerations for PWS adults. Generally, they support the viewpoint of Greenswag (1984a) that close supervision will almost always be needed to control food accessibility, and that few will be able to achieve fully independent living status.

Testimonial accounts of more independent-living situations are provided by Marlett (1991) in a paper presenting the views of young adults with PWS. Clearly, Marlett's volunteers displayed normal aspirations toward adult independence and concomitant activities and responsibilities. While the prognosis for independence has been poor in the past, parents and service providers must be reminded of the normalcy of the drive for independence among young adults with PWS.

James and Willott (1989) discuss a number of influences on placement decisions (Table 3.1). They point out that the ideal

**Table 3.1** Influences on residential placement decisions

| Influences |
|---|
| Parental age |
| Burn-out |
| Lifestyle implications |
| Family expectations |
| Social pressures |
| Lack of respite |
| Crisis management |
| Over-protection |
| Desire for independence |
| Social policy |
| Available funding |
| Categories and labels |
| Level of ability |
| Community options |
| Prognostic information |

*Source*: James and Willott (1989).

**Table 3.2** Needs of persons with Prader–Willi Syndrome

| Needs |
|---|
| Dietary and nutritional guidance |
| Adjusted family-eating patterns |
| Food-access controls |
| Social involvement |
| Occupational activity |
| Medical monitoring |
| Community-living skills |
| Advocacy and support |
| Physical activity |
| Sexuality counselling |
| Continuing-education opportunities |
| Transportation |
| Respite care |
| Spiritual opportunities |
| Guardianship |
| Wills |

*Adapted from*: James and Willott (1989).

would be for families to plan for residential change proactively, rather than making a decision in reaction to a crisis situation. The list of influences was generated from interviews with parents and agency personnel with residential concerns for PWS adults. It should not be considered exhaustive, but rather indicative of some of the factors influencing decisions in some PWS families. In support of the need for holistic planning, there is a list of needs of persons with PWS (Table 3.2), to help focus discussion when determining programme directions and support needs.

## WORK ACTIVITIES

Greenswag (1984a) found 45% of her PWS population to be involved in a sheltered workshop setting, 3.9% in a government or private business, 2.6% to be working as volunteers, and 2.2% working in the home. A further 35.3% were not working, and 10.3% did not respond to this question. Greenswag acknowledges there may have been some confusion over the term 'rehabilitation', with its physical, medical, and vocational inferences, in response to this section of the questionnaire.

In several instances, where there was unlimited access to food, maladaptive behaviours were seen as a barrier to job placement. In general, the effectiveness of workshop services was related to patient, understanding professionals. Sulzbacher *et al.* (1981) point out that from reports from sheltered workshops for developmentally-delayed persons, only minimal special considerations related to food availability and food theft need to be given to PWS trainees. Greenswag concluded that 'sheltered workshops provided the most opportunities for productive occupational activity'. The Prader–Willi Syndrome Association of America goes a step further in stating that 'sheltered workshops generally provide the only employment possibilities' ('The Gathered View', 1990b).

Review of the case studies (n=17) presented by James and Willott (1989), however, reveals that only 35% were attending sheltered workshops. Another 24% were employed to some degree. Their jobs included: part-time peer counsellor at a rehabilitation centre, part-time helper in a video shop, full-time worker in a restaurant operated by an association for mentally handicapped persons, and full-time worker with Goodwill Enterprises for the Handicapped. The remainder were either at home (24%), registered as full-time students (12%), or in undetermined situations (6%). Marlett's (1991) testimonial accounts of young people also describe their self-perceived employment successes, including work as a chambermaid, assistant lifeguard, office helper, farm worker, paper carrier, and aluminium-tin recycler. While all of these were supported work situations to some degree, they were nevertheless community-based work activities providing meaningful alternatives to sheltered workshops.

While no information could be found on job-task performance or PWS worker characteristics, the research of Nardella *et al.* (1983) is noteworthy for its possible implications. After measuring activity levels of 12 PWS individuals at a two-week summer camp, they concluded that there is a 'wide range of physical activity levels among PWS persons', and that 'it is not valid to stereotype such individuals when describing their physical activity levels'. Although Nardella *et al.* were dealing with a recreational setting, their conclusion may have significance for the employment setting. If physical activity levels are a function of personal characteristics, then size and weight alone should not be determining factors in assigning work activities, i.e., obesity should not necessarily dictate more sedentary tasks.

## SUMMARY

While medical and allied health personnel must be called upon to maintain the physical well-being of persons with PWS, professionals from the social sciences must assist with personal-social-behavioural management in the context of home and community. With community living and increasing longevity, quality-of-life issues will require multidisciplinary involvement and a holistic perspective.

This chapter has described some of the behavioural and non-medical management issues associated with PWS and the types of strategies that have been developed. A number of points can be made:

- Despite some common symptoms among people with PWS, there is wide variability in behaviour. Individuals should not be stereotyped in terms of social and psychological characteristics because of the diagnosis. There is variability also in cognitive performance, social behaviours, and recreational skills.
- There is some indication that the degree of obesity is related to a variety of performance levels; however, it is also suggested that this is correlated with cognitive ability. Whether this is a direct result of underlying genetic predisposition, or whether such behaviour is a secondary outcome of biochemical and physiological aberration is not yet clear. However, it is important to recognize that control of eating behaviours early in life may have some impact on motivation, attention, and the development of cognitive abilities, and therefore on levels of educational performance.
- Because of the above, parents should recognize that it is important to involve multidisciplinary personnel in developing and deciding strategies for handling a particular child. The importance of recognizing individual variability and planning to meet the needs accordingly, are critical.
- There is also variability in language. While there may be speech problems resulting from hypotonic musculature of mouth and face anomalies, certain aspects of language may be relatively well developed. In particular, language comprehension may be further advanced than speech production or the use of expressive language.
- There appears to be a high frequency of emotional outbursts among PWS children – but also lethargy and apathy. In terms of emotional outbursts, which often are related to food issues in the community or home, behavioural management techniques have shown some initial success. This area needs to be explored much further.
- Because of the compulsive aspects of eating, problems of normalization and integration into the community are particularly difficult in many PWS children. This is especially clear in relation to school environments.
- It is apparent that students with PWS can complete public education and go on to hold jobs in the community, usually of a semi-skilled or unskilled nature. It is difficult to predict

who will be successful. Training and employment become major issues as longevity increases.

- Perhaps because of the major problems of PWS, such as weight control and behaviour management, the issue of residential or home placement is a major challenge. In Canada, a diverse range of opportunities exists to match the different levels of children's functioning. One disturbing trend noticed elsewhere is the setting up of very large residential facilities for PWS children and adults *en masse*. The history of congregate-care facilities has not been a positive one. In the field of health and allied social community control it has not brought about the development that is known to be possible.

  While a residential facility may take care of some of the difficulties associated with home management, relieve stress on parents, and be relatively cost-efficient, evidence suggests that such facilities do not enhance individualized development or respond to client variability, or enable people to maximize their contact with community environments, resulting in minimal social learning and eventual community placement. If PWS children are not to be treated in a natural environment or among people with different disabilities, then very small units of about five persons should be employed. A wide range of individual care should be supplied, and staff involved should be experienced in the development of individualized programming.
- One of the major secondary effects of PWS is the amount of stress among family members. It seems apparent that stress management and control should feature early in the development of family planning.
- There is a wide range of variability in recreation and leisure time behaviour of individuals with PWS, which provides opportunities for a variety of social, motor, and cognitive learning.

# Chapter 4

# Characteristics of Canadian PWS children

This chapter discusses descriptive and demographic aspects of PWS child characteristics obtained in a survey study of PWS families in western Canada (James, 1987). The study (n=51) was premised on the need to establish a profile of Canadian PWS child and parent characteristics, and to examine home and community-based interventions (Chapters 6, 7, 8) in the light of existing social policy. As little normative data are available for the PWS population, it was considered important to establish a profile of PWS physical and performance characteristics across ages, and to look at aspects of the developmental sequelae in this syndrome. (The term 'child' is used here to denote a relationship with the parent, regardless of age; distinction is made between 'child' and 'adult' only where age is pertinent to the discussion.)

## SEX DISTRIBUTION

While early writers (Hoefnagel *et al.*, 1967; Cohen and Gorlin, 1969; Wannarachue *et al.*, 1975) suggested an imbalance in the PWS sex ratio favouring males, more recently it has been suggested that the distribution is similar between the sexes (Greenswag, 1984a; Zellweger, 1983). The sample in the present study was slightly skewed in favour of females (29 females, 22 males), but should not be generalized to indicate an imbalance in sexual distribution. An examination of the sex ratios in major studies (e.g., Greenswag, 1984a; Hall and Smith, 1972; Hermann, 1981; Holm, 1981a) suggests that numerical differences are more likely the result of sampling error.

## AGE

The mean age of James's (1987) total sample was 16.8 years, with 59% under 19 years of age. The range of ages is similar to that reported in the major studies referred to in the previous paragraph. Bray *et al.* (1983) also report an upper age of 37 years. Greenswag (1984a), however, found 28 PWS subjects in their 30s, three in their 40s, and one aged 64. Goldman (1988) presents the case of a 69-year-old female, which is believed to be the oldest subject on record. While earlier clinical literature (e.g., Hoefnagel *et al.*, 1967; Zellweger and Schneider, 1968) suggested a reduced life expectancy due to complications from gross obesity, it seems reasonable to expect that greater longevity will occur with early identification and better weight management.

## ETHNIC BACKGROUND

One subject was a Canadian Indian; the remainder were Caucasian. All were at least first-generation Canadians. While the early case literature presented mainly Caucasian subjects, it must be recognized that those observations came from European and North American countries. Butler *et al.* (1982) noted the small number of Black people with PWS, and questioned whether there was a true difference or whether this was due to under-reporting. DeFrance *et al.* (1984) examined the international literature and found only two cases of Black people, and concluded that racial differences did seem to be present. More recently, however, Hispanics, Blacks, and American Indians were represented in Greenswag's (1984a) North American survey. The international literature now contains reports from almost all European countries, some Latin American countries, Israel, South Africa, Australia, India, and Japan (Zellweger, 1983).

## PREGNANCY AND BIRTH

There is some variation in characteristics of pregnancy described in the literature to date. Maternal gestational problems were reported by Hall and Smith (1972) to be infrequent, minor, and inconsistent. Similarly, Dunn (1968) found that pregnancy was usually unremarkable, although four out of nine mothers had vaginal bleeding in the first trimester, and both diminished and augmented foetal movements were noted. Low levels of 'foetal vigour' have been reported by Hall and Smith (94%), Bray *et al.* (1983) (84%), and Butler *et al.* (1986) (81–90%); the present study, on the other hand, found an 'absence of intrauterine movement' in only 43% of the cases. Inconsistency in terminology and possible memory distortion from the use of retrospective data likely contribute to the lower response in the present investigation.

Full-term pregnancies occurred in 60% of the cases for which information was available. Other investigators have reported shortened mean gestational periods (Butler *et al.*, 1986; Dunn *et al.*, 1981), or prolonged gestation (Cohen, 1969; Hoefnagel *et al.*, 1967), and have recognized that either can occur (Zellweger, 1981). Seventeen percent of the present sample were reported to have been premature by greater than 21 days, and 23% of mothers reported terms extending an additional 10–21 days. Generalizations about shortened or prolonged gestation should be made with qualification, since either is possible and occur with some regularity. One in five mothers in the study reported previous miscarriages, and one in ten indicated vaginal bleeding.

Only 6% of mothers in the present study had Caesarean sections; Butler *et al.* (1986) reported 18%, and Holm (1981a) and Dunn *et al.* (1981) each reported 15%. Breech presentations were noted by Butler *et al.* (1986), Bray *et al.* (1983), Dunn *et al.* (1981), Hall and Smith (1972), and Holm (1981a), among others, ranging from 22–40% of PWS cases. In the study by James (1987), the figure was only marginally lower at 20%.

## NEONATAL CHARACTERISTICS

Hypotonia was regarded by Holm (1981a) as one of the obligatory manifestations required for a firm PWS diagnosis. Consistent with this observation, Butler *et al.* (1986) presented summary data from seven significant North American studies in which hypotonia was described as a universal characteristic. The 100% figure reported in the present study is consistent with this requirement for clinical diagnosis.

A poor suck was also designated by Holm (1981a) as a requisite for diagnosis, and occurred in 97% of the cases in her study. Other authors report a similar high incidence for poor sucking or general neonatal feeding difficulty (Butler *et al.*, 1986; Dunn, 1968; Hall and Smith, 1972; Zellweger, 1981; Zellweger and Schneider, 1968). Parents in the present study noted a weak or absent sucking reflex in 94% of their PWS children, resulting in tube feeding or other assistance in 64% of the cases. This latter figure is lower than the 98% figure reported by Holm. The difference can be accounted for at least in part by the wording of the data collection instruments. The questionnaire used in the present study only identified 'tube feeding required', whereas Holm presented additional detail on types of nipples required for bottle-feeding. With the exception of two of James's (1987) families who reported a good appetite for their infant, the rest consistently described a 'concern for thriving' during the neonatal period.

A weak or absent cry was described for 91% of the subjects in this study. Holm (1981a) previously reported a figure of 88%. Several of the present subjects did not cry until six to nine months of age. While it was the consensus of the physicians in Holm's study that this symptom was not directly related to the hypotonia, several parents in the present study described the onset of crying as being related to minor physical trauma: 'no cry until six months when head bumped mother's front teeth', 'cried at two months when she had her first needle', 'absent cry until three months – induced by EMG needle'.

A delay in crying response may be related to the decreased pain sensitivity that has been noted by several investigators (Greenswag, 1984a; Holm, 1981b; Wett, 1985), although this is usually described in relation to the adult population. As an infant's cry is the primary means of communication with parents, the inability of many PWS infants to communicate normally raises many questions of psychological interest with respect to satisfaction of physical needs, emotional nurturance, and possible effects of deprivation.

## DEVELOPMENTAL MILESTONES

In this study it was found that developmental milestones were generally delayed. There were no significant sex differences for sitting, crawling, or walking. Interestingly, 62% of the parents who responded to the question on crawling provided additional comments on the unorthodox nature of their child's experience. In summary, the child either went directly from sitting to standing (3%), rolled everywhere (14%), wiggled on the stomach (7%), or, more commonly, scooted on the buttocks (38%). This last was variously described as a 'sit-crawl', 'bum-slide', 'sitting-sideways crawl', 'bum-scoot', or 'bum-shuffle'.

Information relating to delays in the developmental milestones of PWS subjects in this study is consistent with existing literature reports. The characteristic stages of development (Zellweger, 1981) were evidenced, with the exception of the two individuals who had good appetites from birth. The range of delay in developmental milestones is consistent with the findings of Butler *et al.* (1986) and Holm (1981a), and is illustrated in comparison with major child developmental scales (e.g., Bayley Scale of Infant Development, Denver Developmental Screening Test), in Table 4.1.

The developmental delays documented in PWS are strong arguments for the provision of infant stimulation programmes, yet only 29% of parents in this study had utilized this service. For the parents of older subjects, infant stimulation programmes might not have been an option, as little in the way of early intervention was available before 1970 in Canada (Shipe, 1984). On the other hand, one mother lamented the inaccessibility of an infant stimulation programme for her child as it was operating on a first-come-first-served basis because of government cut-backs.

The relationship between developmental delays and cognitive

**Table 4.1** A comparison of cognitive development and physical developmental milestones for two PWS children of suspected normal intelligence[a]

| *Subject* | *CA* | *PPVT-R stand. score* | *PPVT-R %le equiv.* | *Sit* | *Crawl (in months)* | *Walk* |
|---|---|---|---|---|---|---|
| 1 | 3.7 | 100 | 50 | 11 | 14 | 20 |
| 2 | 5.6 | 100 | 50 | 8 | 11 | 18 |
| Bayley Scale of Infant Development[b] | | | | 6.6 | 7.1 | 11.7 |
| Denver Developmental Screening Test[b] | | | | 5.5 | . . . | 12.1 |

a – with chromosome-15 deletion
b – 50th %le norms

development is of interest. Butler *et al.* (1986) report greater delays in crawling and walking for PWS children with chromosome-15 deletions than for PWS children without deletions. On the other hand, intelligence quotients were reported to be significantly higher for the deletion group. Similarly, in the present study, the two children with chromosome-15 deletions who scored at the 50th percentile on the Peabody Picture Vocabulary Test (PPVT-R) were substantially delayed in their physical milestones (Table 4.1). In each case the subject was below the fifth percentile on the Bayley Scale of Infant Development, or below the tenth percentile on the Denver Developmental Screening Test for the appropriate age group.

## HEIGHT AND WEIGHT

The age of onset of obesity reported in this study indicates a broader range (one to ten years) than usually reported (e.g., Holm, 1981a; Nugent and Holm, 1981). The mean and median ages for onset of obesity (3.9 years and 3.2 years, respectively), however, are certainly within the usual parameters. The synopsis provided by the Prader–Willi Syndrome Association (1984), suggests that obesity generally becomes prominent between six months and five years of age if food intake is not controlled. While obesity was not specifically defined for parents in this study, their subjective figures are only slightly above the clinical observations obtained by Dunn *et al.* (1981), who reported that weight became significantly excessive (greater than two standard deviations above the mean for height-age) at a mean age of 35.7 months.

While Greenswag (1984a) reported significant differences for height and weight between sexes, the present study revealed no overall differences of significance between sexes for present weight, high weight, or low weight in the last year. In contrast to Greenswag's data, no significant differences were found between sexes for adult weights; the difference for height between the sexes, however, was significant, with males being taller.

The calculation of the pondostatural index (PSI=weight in pounds/height in inches) is helpful for comparisons of height-weight data across groups. (Imperial measurements are used here to facilitate comparison with American data.) The scattergram of PSI scores for PWS children contained in Figure 4.1 presents an accelerated pattern of weight gain in comparison to Canadian children under age 18. This pattern is well recognized in the PWS literature. Figure 4.1 also reflects the initial concern for thriving (under age three), although there were

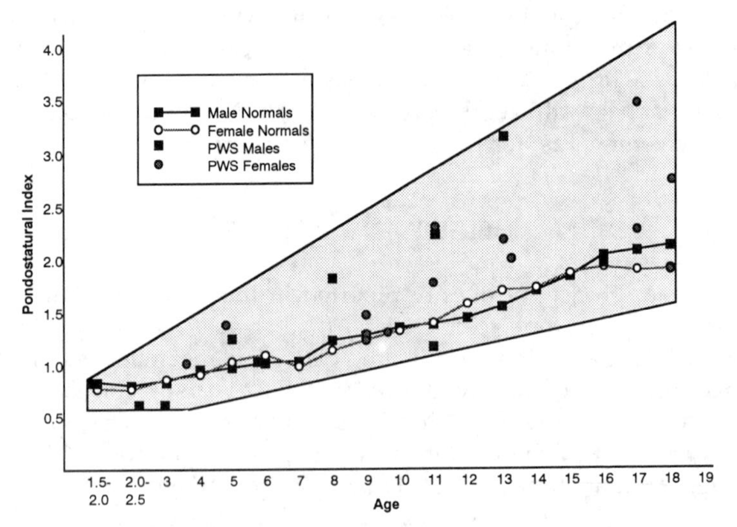


**Figure 4.1** Pondostatural indices for PWS children under the age of 18 compared to the norms for Canadian children.

only a few cases at this age. Based on this small sample, males appear to gain weight more quickly than females. This observation is tentative, however, pending the calculation of PSI scores for larger numbers of PWS children. It is notable that the precocious male pattern of weight gain in childhood is consistent with that of the adult population reported by Greenswag (1984a).

A scattergram of adult scores imposed on Greenswag's (1984a) American data shows a broad scatter of indices, with standard deviation increasing with age until the 30s (Figure 4.2). If excessive weight does contribute to earlier mortality, one

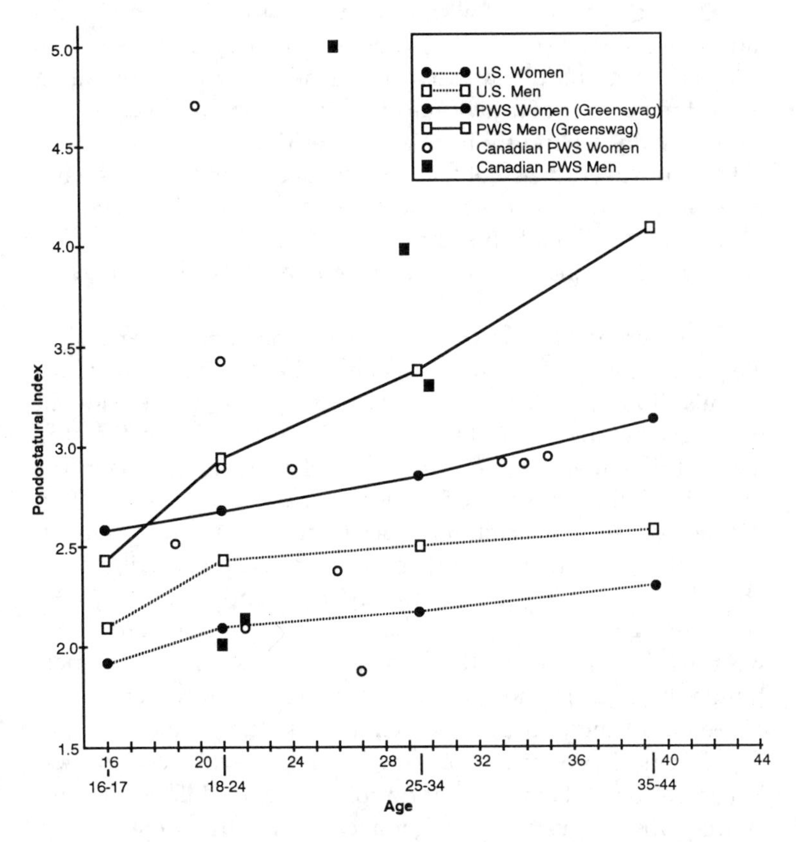


**Figure 4.2** Comparison of PWS pondostatural indices and those of Greenswag (adapted from Greenswag, 1984a, with kind permission).

would expect PSI scores for heavier, older subjects to begin to regress toward the mean, thus lowering the mean in advanced age as the scores for the few subjects above age 30 in this study tend to suggest. The highest index was 5.0 for a 26-year-old male (300lb/136kg and 60in/152cm tall) who was hospitalized for weight control at the time of the study. The next highest index was 4.73 for a 22-year-old female (289lb/131kg and 61in/155cm). Of the adults, only three exceeded five feet in height, with the tallest being only five-feet-four inches (162.56cm). Of interest is the fact that 64% of the indices in this study fall below the corresponding American PWS mean, and that 23% further fall below the norms for the American population in general. While the James (1987) study is too small to calculate meaningful Canadian PWS means, it is encouraging to see the number of individuals for whom weight-management strategies do apparently have some positive effect. This observation, however, does not take into consideration the possibility of ethnic, cultural, climatic, or other differences between the American and Canadian samples, which could reflect in differences in eating and activity habits – and hence weight management.

As numerous parents were intuitively managing their child's weight without professional assistance, these findings challenge Holm's (1981a) statement that obesity should be considered necessary before a firm diagnosis of PWS is made. In fact, the mean differential between the onset of obesity and diagnosis for males in the present study was only .55 of a year, suggesting that for some male children obesity may not have been an essential manifestation for diagnosis of PWS. The criteria for obesity, as Holm suggests, must be different for diagnosis at an early age. She proposes that the tendency toward rapid weight-gain, as evidenced in a sudden increase in weight percentile, be used in the preschool years (children under age 5). Three out of the four preschoolers in this study, however, had not shown disproportionate weight gain, as evidenced in their PSI scores being below the norm for Canadian children in general. Hence obesity at a younger age may not be essential. This viewpoint is supported by the recent work of Greenswag and Alexander, who found that obesity at the time of diagnosis was significantly less common among an early diagnosis group (0–36 months) ('The Gathered View', 1990a).

Annual weight fluctuation for adults with PWS in this study averaged 25.7lb (11.6kg), with a high differential of 150lb (68kg) in the most extreme case. The differential between high and low weights in the last 12 months ranged from 4lb to 110lb (1.81 to 49.9kg). In one case (male, age 26) the lowest weight in the last 12 months was 230lb (104.3kg). The highest weight was 340lb (154.2kg), and the present weight was 300lb (136kg). Total weight fluctuation was, therefore, 150lb (68kg) in the last year. In another case (male, age 23) 125lb (56.7kg) were lost over the preceding 24 months. Excluding these two extreme cases, for those PWS subjects over the age of 17 years for whom data from weight charts were available, the mean total weight-loss/gain in the last 12 months was 19.5lb (8.8kg); the mean weight fluctuation was 25.7lb (11.6kg) (n=19).

Such fluctuation attests to the ease with which persons with PWS put on weight. From a psycho-social perspective, the fluctuation in weight – rather than the obesity itself – may be an important factor. Not only do PWS individuals face the stigma associated with obesity, but they are also likely to be subject to vacillations in physical well-being, self-concept, and social acceptance associated with recurrent cycles of weight gain and weight loss. If individuals with PWS have an organic predisposition toward obesity, behavioural intervention for weight management should recognize the reality of significant fluctuation and cyclical patterns.

In the past, the prognosis for persons with PWS has generally been poor; death as a teenager or young adult due to cardiorespiratory problems associated with gross obesity has been described (Laurance *et al.*, 1981; Marshall *et al.*, 1981). Presently, the oldest cases on record appear to be women aged 64 (Greenswag, 1984a) and 69 years (Goldman, 1988). Most studies, however, report an upper-age range in the 30s with a few affected persons in the 40s. As the oldest subjects in the present study were maintaining constant weight and were not suffering significant medical problems when interviewed, one can be optimistic about increasing longevity. As many of the early studies were based on institutionalized populations, the placements may have been a factor in the weight-management problems, and hence longevity. One teenage girl in the present study, for example, was reported by her parents to have entered a provincial mental health institution for disturbed adolescents at age 13 weighing 117lb (53kg); she was discharged at age 17 weighing 228lb (103.5kg). Similarly, a PWS lady in her mid-30s, re-integrated into community living from a provincial resource institution for persons with mental handicaps, weighed 169lb (76.7kg) at the time of discharge, and only 124lb (56.2kg) two years later at the time of this study.

## OTHER CLINICAL FEATURES

### Mouth shape

Zellweger (1981), in discussing first-phase characteristics of PWS, described a triangular-shaped mouth resembling an inverted 'V', an appearance sometimes referred to as 'fish-mouth' or 'shark-mouth'. Holm (1981a) similarly described a triangular mouth as a 'classical facial feature'. Only 28% of the PWS subjects in the present study, however, were described as having a 'down-curved' mouth. Hanson (1981) suggested that a triangular mouth is secondary to poor development of the jaw. Those subjects with this feature in the present study ranged from four through thirty years of age, suggesting the condition may be constant throughout the life-span of an individual. One mother, however, noted that the condition existed at an early age and became less obvious as her child grew older. The low incidence of a down-curved mouth found in the present investigation is in contrast to irregularities of the mouth shape indicated by Holm as a classical facial feature in most PWS persons.

### Speech problems

Zellweger (1988) identified delayed speech, often accompanied by articulation defects, as a phase-two characteristic of PWS. Holm (1981a) found that only 19% of her respondents had speech problems, compared with 40% in the present study. As screening for speech and language services are quite routinely provided for children in Canadian public education, usually beginning at the kindergarten level (age 5), it is more likely that such problems will be identified today than a decade ago.

## Scoliosis

The 35%-rate of scoliosis found in the present study falls short of the 87%-rate of structural scoliosis (greater than ten degrees) reported by Laurnen (1981). Laurnen, however, utilized physical and radiological examination in a PWS clinic setting. Other investigators have reported much lower incidences. It is suspected that the 35%-figure presented here is due to under-reporting, as several parents lacked an understanding of scoliosis.

## Skin-picking

Information on skin-picking in the present study was derived from anecdotal parent reports and comments added to the questionnaires, and may also represent under-reporting. Direct observation of PWS subjects, however, suggests a rate considerably lower than the 81% reported by Holm (1981a) from a survey of parents and physicians. Butler *et al.* (1986) present data for the specific 'habit of picking sores'. They report 76–83% of their subjects to have this habit.

Unfortunately, the severity of skin-picking is seldom reported. It may range from chronic itching with scratching, to habitual picking at sores, to more self-injurious picking and gouging. Holm (1981b) reports that subjects may actually create sores on the intact skin. In one such case in the present study, a young lady was observed to have exposed skin on her legs and arms dotted with bluish bruises and scabbed sores. Without a specific measurement scale, skin-picking was observed to range from what could be considered a mild form of chronic rubbing and scratching to the more severe case just noted. Such observations were usually corroborated by parental descriptions. Review of the skin-picking respondents in the present study suggests that it occurs with relatively similar frequency across all ages.

In terms of prevention, children at younger ages who

displayed skin-picking were dressed appropriately in order to cover their arms, legs, and neck areas. In an extreme case, long gloves were worn at school during the day. Of primary concern was the fear of infection from chronic picking at cuts, sores, and surgical wounds. This same fear was expressed by parents of adult dependants who were chronic skin-pickers, although none reported cases of complications from such feared infections. It is not uncommon for PWS subjects to scratch at insect bites or minor skin lesions until an open sore results. Various topical applications were used, primarily among the adult PWS subjects, although more behavioural-management strategies and cosmetics were being sought.

Little information is available on clinical treatment of skin-picking. Self-picking, however, was a specific target behaviour at the Prader–Willi Syndrome Project at Dubnoff Center in California (Freitag *et al.*, 1986). Self-picking was defined as 'any behaviour including picking or pinching self, that leaves a mark that is purple, or that breaks the skin and causes bleeding, or that leaves fingernails ragged'. Data obtained for nine residents over a four-and-one-half-year period showed an average decrease of 73% in frequency of occurrence, the greatest decrease of the 14 targeted behaviours. The authors reported that self-picking was eliminated in only one client, suggesting the persistence of this characteristic despite external intervention over a considerable time period.

## Secondary sexual characteristics

The lack of primary sexual development has been commented on by virtually all writers on PWS. In terms of secondary characteristics 90% of the present sample over 12 years of age were reported to have axillary and pubic hair, and 27% facial hair. The latter was often described as scant, and occurred with equal frequency between sexes. Laurance *et al.* (1981) also reported axillary and pubic hair to be sparse in both sexes in their study, although no figures were given.

## COGNITIVE DEVELOPMENT

The Peabody Picture Vocabulary Test – Revised (PPVT-R) (Dunn and Dunn, 1981) was administered to PWS subjects in the present study as a quick assessment of verbal ability. The chronological age-range of subjects (n=31) was 3 years, 7 months to 36 years, 9 months; the age equivalency (i.e., mental age) ranged from 3 to 24 years. Scores tended to decline with age in a fan-like pattern, bottoming in the late teenage years (Figure 4.3). The summary data suggest generally low achievement. In terms of stanines, 20 (64.5%) scored at the first stanine, 7 (22.6%) at the second stanine, 2 (6.5%) at the fourth stanine, and 2 (6.5%) at the fifth stanine. In percentile terms, the highest four subjects ranked at the 34th, 37th, and 50th (2) percentiles. Chronological ages were 30 years, 2 months; 4 years, 1 month; 5 years, 6 months; and 3 years, 2 months; respectively. In more general terms, 12.5% of the scores were in the average range; 31% were moderately low, that is greater than one standard deviation from the mean of the general population; and 56% were extremely low (>2 SD). No significant differences were found between the sexes on PPVT-R performance.

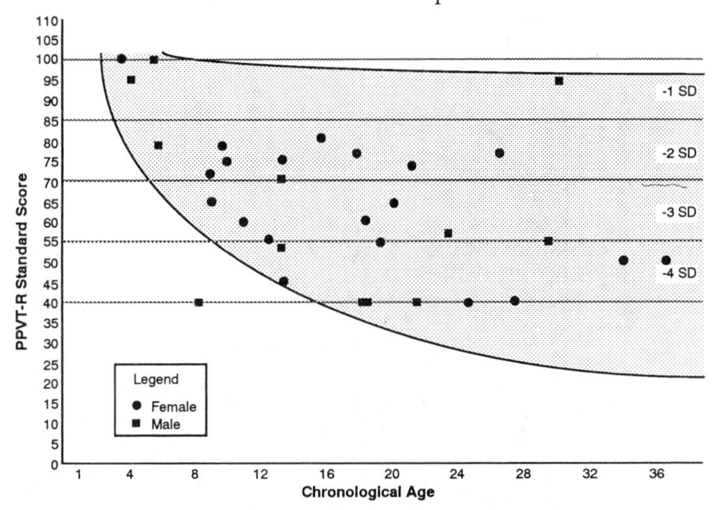


**Figure 4.3** Scattergram of PPVT-R standard scores.

When the data are collapsed or reduced to a few categories, a decline in performance is readily observable. Figure 4.4 presents the PPVT-R data by age quartiles, and Figure 4.5 by developmental stages. Both histograms show the highest performance in the youngest age grouping followed by a considerable performance decline, which then remains relatively constant across the other ages.

The numerous reports of PWS subjects being 'highly manipulative', 'sneaky', and 'quick', do not fit the general impression of individuals with mental handicaps. Despite the fact that the early literature included mental handicap as a primary descriptor of PWS (e.g., Dunn, 1968; Hoefnagel *et al.*, 1967; Jancar, 1971; Prader *et al.*, 1956; Zellweger and Schneider, 1968), more recent work has indicated specific cognitive deficits akin to those of individuals with learning disabilities (Crnic *et al.*, 1980; Gabel *et al.*, 1986; Warren and Hunt, 1981).

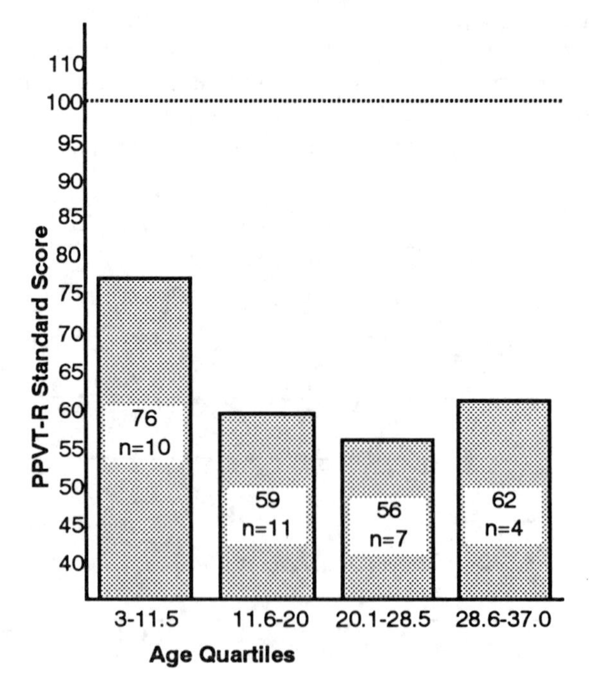


**Figure 4.4** PPVT-R standard scores by age quartiles.

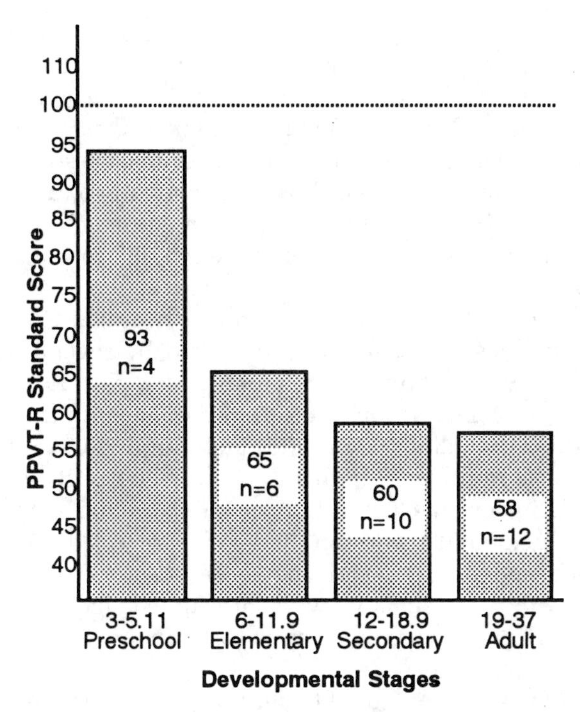


**Figure 4.5** PPVT-R standard scores by developmental stages.

To the extent that the PPVT-R is a measurement of achievement and of one facet of general intelligence (Umberger, 1984) the range of scores evidenced in this study is consistent with other reports of general intelligence (Butler *et al.*, 1986; Holm, 1981a). Neuro-psychological evidence (Gabel *et al.*, 1986) indicates that the most striking area of impairment for PWS subjects is on performance tasks involving the auditory modality (perception involving hearing). If this is so, the PPVT-R results, with their emphasis on auditory-receptive vocabulary, may possibly be low estimates of achievement and general intelligence.

While karyotype (i.e., chromosome constitution) data were not available for most subjects in this study, it is worth noting that the two children identified in Table 4.4 as being within the normal range of intelligence on the PPVT-R both had chromosome-15 deletions. This is consistent with the results of a comparison of psychological test performance on chromosome-15 deletion and non-deletion groups by Butler *et al.* (1986). They found the average IQ for the group without the deletion to be significantly lower, but qualified their results as tentative pending the study of larger samples with more uniform testing procedures. While the data for the above-mentioned two cases lends support to the findings of Butler *et al.*, more research is needed on the relationship of intelligence to karyotype in individuals with PWS.

The observation that the intellectual performance of PWS children declines with age has been noted by several writers (Crnic *et al.*, 1980; Dunn, 1968; Holm and Pipes, 1976). It is possible that the interaction of the environment with the physical and allied disabilities contributes importantly to a decline in intellectual performance. If this is so, the prospect of remediation is enhanced. Observation of scores falling within the normal range of intelligence on the PPVT-R revealed three subjects to be under age 6, and one to be at age 30. The latter impressed the investigator with his knowledge of music, religion, and current events, despite living in a relatively unstimulating environment.

As subjects were not studied over time, individual decline in performance with age cannot be addressed. The scattergram of PPVT-R scores (Figure 4.3), however, suggests a particular group pattern of performance decline with advancing age. Scores tend to decline in a fan-like array, reaching their lower limits toward the late teenage years. The histograms presented in Figures 4.4 and 4.5 graphically demonstrate the early decline in performance with age. This observation is consistent with that of Crnic *et al.* (1980), but requires further testing with larger samples and a variety of instruments. It should be noted that the three preschoolers within the normal range all had the advantage of early intervention programmes.

Since longevity for PWS individuals now appears to be greater than previously thought, the question of age-related performance decline versus a syndrome-specific early onset in performance decline needs to be explored. The work of Crnic *et al.* (1980), showing IQ decline with increased weight and advancing age in PWS children, suggests that cognitive performance peaks at a relatively young age. As few adult-aged subjects in this study had the opportunity for continuing education, or even the benefit of intellectually challenging job tasks, the stimulus for future cognitive growth in the 20s and 30s age groups may be appreciably environmental. Longitudinal follow-up is needed, particularly to monitor individual progress following early intervention for weight control.

The authors are in accord with Hall and Smith (1972) and Holm (1981a) in believing that mental handicap is a frequent, but not necessarily requisite, feature of PWS. It may be that specific as yet unidentified learning deficits inhibit the learning process, thus underscoring the need for intervention with appropriate teaching methodologies. At the same time, developmental delays may contribute to poor motor performance, diminished social acceptance, lack of promotion, and motivational difficulties. Undoubtedly the problem compounds even further with inappropriate educational placements and the lack of necessary syndrome-specific supports. Thus, limitations in cognitive performance mistakenly may be viewed as mental handicap of genetic origin rather than as environmentally induced.

Some authors (Thompson *et al.*, 1988) assert that 'most children with PWS should be considered functionally retarded regardless of IQ test scores', but this position is taken in order to meet criteria determining eligibility for services. This is unfortunate, since actual performance across a range of skills should determine the programmes that are received. (Labelling and access to services is discussed in Chapter 8.)

## SOCIAL DEVELOPMENT

Some authors make the point that the psycho-social rather than medical aspects are the main concerns in the management of PWS (Hermann, 1981; Greenswag, 1984a). Children with PWS usually fall behind their peers in social-skill development (Neason, 1978), and present behaviour-management problems by the teenage years (Leconte, 1981).

The Progress Assessment Chart (PAC) (Gunzburg, 1977) was utilized in the present study in an attempt to quantify aspects of social development. Comparisons across PAC domains (Table

**Table 4.2** Progress Assessment Chart (PAC) of social development summary results

| *Social Competence Index (SCI)* | *Range* | *Mean* | *Median* | *Mode* |
|---|---|---|---|---|
| Self-help | 32–220 | 115.9 | 110.0 | 108 |
| Communication | 25–400 | 178.2 | 149.8 | 150 |
| Occupational | 14–375 | 122.2 | 117.2 | 86 |
| Social | 27–286 | 132.8 | 120.5 | 93 |
| General | 44–286 | 133.5 | 119.5 | 79 |
| n=42 | | | | |

4.2) indicate a broad range of response within all domains; mean and median scores above the norms for mentally handicapped persons in general in all domains; and significantly stronger assessment in the area of communication skills. This last-mentioned is opposite to the trend for persons with mental handicaps in general (Gunzburg, 1968). Given that mental handicap has been a common descriptor in PWS, comparisons were made with appropriate subgroups of diagnostically undifferentiated persons with mental handicaps. The fact that the average attainment scores were consistently above the norm of 100 suggests that persons with PWS as a group function better in the areas of social competence on the PAC than do their counterparts with mental handicaps. The range of scores in all domains, however, underscores the variability in response from quite handicapped to superior for each particular subgroup.

To the degree that social development may be a factor of cognitive ability, the results of the PAC assessment appear to support the viewpoint that mental handicap is not necessarily a requisite of the syndrome (Hall and Smith, 1972; Holm, 1981a), and that there are differentiated strengths and weaknesses (Crnic *et al.*, 1980; Gabel *et al.*, 1986; Warren and Hunt, 1981).

Whereas Gunzburg (1968) sees a trend for self-help, occupation and socialization skills to be better developed than communication skills among mentally handicapped children in general, the opposite was observed for the PWS sample in the present study. Gunzburg points out that when 'able to dress and wash himself and to eat properly and occupy himself, the mentally handicapped child is a less constant liability and embarrassment and requires less supervision'. In contrast, the PWS children in this study were assessed lower in self-help, socialization, and occupational skills, and often seemed to be a liability or embarrassment in need of supervision. A lack of skills related to self-care, eating, and occupation are implied by Gunzburg to be related to potentially stressful demands on the parents. There were no statistically significant correlations, however, between parental stress levels and PAC domain scores.

The PAC was created to assist in designing realistic and efficient developmental education programmes (Gunzburg, 1983). The uneven average attainment of skills across domains suggests the need to address weaker areas through special-education programming. Self-help, occupational, and social domain components need to be examined for substantial deficits and the lack of opportunity for learning. The higher-average attainment in the communication domain relates most directly to academic successes. Contained within this domain on the PAC 2, for example, are language, money, time measures, writing skills, and reading skills. By contrast, the self-help domain contains table habits, cleanliness, care of clothing, mobility, and health items; socialization includes shopping, social graces, home assistance, financial dealings, and social initiative; and the occupational domain includes manual activities, leisure occupations, and employment.

It is not surprising to see students who are the product of special-education classes who have some successes in academically related areas, as much attention has been paid to remediation of academic deficits in the past. However, the PAC results indicate a need for a more holistic approach to educational programming, emphasizing opportunities for instruction in non-academic areas. Given that individuals with PWS experience considerable peer-relationship problems, for example, more attention should be paid to teaching socialization skills. The implication of this was very poignant in listening to PWS parent concerns. Several parents complained about inappropriate educational programme placements, their children being assigned to various programmes for students with mental handicaps or behaviour disturbances not on the basis of academic performance, but on the basis of social and behavioural considerations.

## DIAGNOSIS

Only one case in the present sample (n=51) was reportedly diagnosed at birth, in 1973. An additional two cases were diagnosed by six months of age. Fifty percent were diagnosed before age six, a further 25% by age 12, another 20% during the teen years, and 5% as adults. Only 11% were identified after age 16, with 32 years being the oldest age at the time of diagnosis (Figure 4.6). The mean age of diagnosis was 7.4 years; the median age was 4.9 years. Males were diagnosed significantly earlier than females.

Parents saw an average of six physicians, including GPs and specialists, before reaching a diagnosis of PWS (mode=2, median=4). Approximately 10% of the couples saw more than 10 physicians. The highest number of medical practitioners reportedly seen was 30, a figure given by a parent whose daughter had not been diagnosed until age 32.

While a few parents received the PWS diagnosis as a result of the initiative of their paediatrician or GP, most had to seek out knowledgeable specialists themselves. In this study, parents were presented with a check-list of symptoms that caused them to persist in their pursuit of diagnosis. Table 4.3 reports their responses, in order of descending frequency. Manifestations related to physical performance capabilities (i.e., muscle devel-

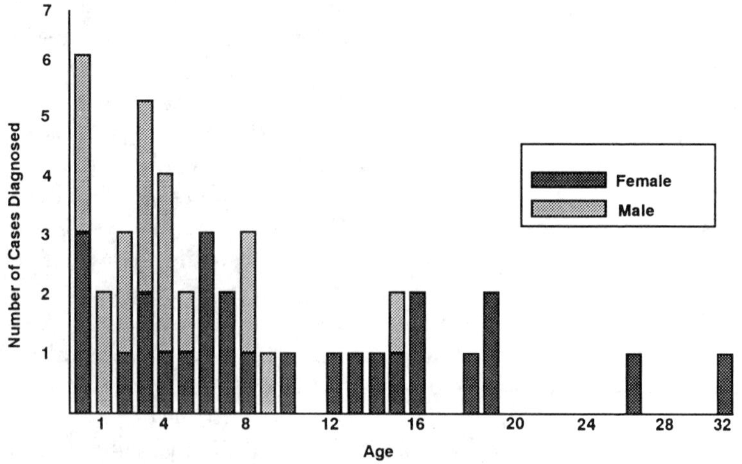


**Figure 4.6** Age and sex of PWS subjects at diagnosis.

**Table 4.3** Symptoms causing parents to seek a diagnosis

| *Symptom* | *Frequency* | *Percent of total sample* |
|---|---|---|
| Muscle development | 34 | 66.7 |
| Motor difficulties | 32 | 62.7 |
| Weight gain | 28 | 54.9 |
| Slow mental development | 26 | 51.0 |
| Over-eating | 25 | 49.0 |
| Behaviour problems | 25 | 49.0 |
| Feeding problems | 23 | 45.1 |
| Speech problems | 21 | 41.2 |
| Eye problems | 17 | 33.3 |
| Social difficulties | 14 | 27.5 |
| Lack of sexual development | 13 | 25.5 |
| n=51 | | |

opment, motor difficulties, and weight gain) were reported with the highest frequency.

The significant difference found between PWS child gender and the average age of diagnosis ($\bar{x}$ males=3.8 years; $\bar{x}$ females=10.0 years) is consistent with the findings of Greenswag (1984a). Greenswag, however, surveyed an adult PWS population and found the mean age of diagnosis to be somewhat older than in the present study ($\bar{x}$ male=11.4 years; $\bar{x}$ female=14.1 years). It is likely that the discrepancy in the mean ages at diagnosis represents, at least in part, improvements in diagnostic criteria in recent years. In Greenswag's sample, 31% of the subjects (n=232) were over the age of 25 years, placing their birth dates prior to 1958. As PWS was not described in the literature until 1956 (Prader *et al.*), there was a diagnostic 'back-log' effect included in her study. By contrast, only 16% of those in the present study were born before that date. Both studies are consistent with clinical observations suggesting that PWS is easier to recognize at a younger age in males than in females (Cohen and Gorlin, 1969; Dunn, 1968; Hoefnagel *et al.*, 1967; Wannarachue *et al.*, 1975).

In terms of the range of ages at diagnosis, the present study is consistent with the findings of other researchers (Butler *et al.*, 1986; Greenswag, 1984a; Hanson, 1981) indicating diagnoses anywhere from birth to mid-30s. Greenswag, for example, reported five subjects diagnosed at birth (2.2%), while the present study identified one (1.9%). The 49% figure for subjects diagnosed before age six in this study is similar to the 50% diagnosed 'before school age' in Hanson's (1981) study. Greenswag found 36% of her subjects diagnosed after age 16, Hanson found 33% diagnosed after age 13, and this investigator found a slightly lower number (22%) after this age.

While the oldest age of diagnosis in this sample occurred during the time of the study in Alberta at the age of 32 years, it can reasonably be expected that improvements in diagnostic techniques and increased awareness will continue to result in earlier diagnoses in the future. The accuracy of diagnosis, however, seems to be directly related to age: the earlier the diagnosis, the more possibility there is for over-inclusion, particularly when there is absence of genetic confirmation. The oldest age of diagnosis reported in the literature concerns Betty, described by Goldman (1988). She was diagnosed at age 67, her condition having gone unrecognized for her previous 48 years in a residential facility in the United States.

It is possible that medical practitioners might overlook sexual features characteristic of PWS, as the lack of sexual development was identified with the least frequency by parents as a reason for seeking a diagnosis. As GPs often respond primarily to identified symptoms, they may not perform a comprehensive medical examination. The other manifestations in Table 4.3 are, in various combinations, common to numerous developmental disorders of childhood. Caution should be exercised, therefore, in inferring relative importance to them in this table. The importance may also vary according to the stage of development. For example, feeding problems are of vital concern in infancy, yet are replaced by a concern for over-eating in the second stage of PWS. Similarly, lack of sexual development may not be a parental concern until it is identified by the child as a concern, usually not until after school entry.

Since obesity is one of the primary descriptors of PWS, the differences between the mean ages of onset of obesity by sex was examined in the present study. While probability did not reach significance, it is interesting that the mean differential between the onset of obesity and age of diagnosis in males was only 0.5 of a year (3.80−3.25), whereas it was 5.74 years (10.0−4.26) for females. Further examination of the number of parents identifying weight as a factor causing them to pursue a medical diagnosis indicated no statistically significant difference between sexes. A possible implication of these data is that obesity in our culture is more acceptable among female special-needs children than among males.

## SIBLINGS

The number of children in the PWS families in this study ranged from one to seven, with one or two siblings being the most common. Included are two situations in which a natural child of an adoptive father, and another of a live-in 'father' were also living in the homes. In no instances, however, were there more than three siblings resident in the home at the time of this study. This can be accounted for by the age and the ordinal position of the PWS child (Table 4.4), that is to say many older siblings had already left the family home. The PWS child was an only child in six instances (12%), and the first-born on 20 occasions (39%). There were 14 cases of the PWS child being the eldest child (27%), and 18 instances when he or she was the youngest (35%), leaving 13 other birth-order situations (26%).

There were no twin births, and only three cases of siblings with other congenital conditions mentioned to the investigator (PKU, undifferentiated mental handicap, heart defect). There were no other known PWS cases within each family.

## CHILD STRESS

The assessment of child stress is complicted by the definition of stress, the methodology chosen to assess it, and the ages of the children. Standardized testing is seldom available for the childhood population, and self-reporting raises a question of validity. The issue is further complicated by the generally impaired cognitive functioning among the PWS population.

Data have been obtained, however, for four young PWS women, all between the ages 18–21 years, who completed the

**Table 4.4** Sibling relationships

| | (%) |
|---|---|
| *Number of children in the home* | |
| Only child | 23.5 |
| One sibling | 27.5 |
| Two siblings | 13.7 |
| Three siblings | 5.9 |
| Four siblings | – |
| Not applicable (child in other residence; independent adults) | 29.4 |
| *Number of children* | |
| Only child | 11.8 |
| One sibling | 33.3 |
| Two siblings | 25.5 |
| Three siblings | 7.8 |
| Four siblings | 7.8 |
| Five siblings | 9.8 |
| Six siblings | 2.0 |
| Unknown | 2.0 |
| *Ordinal position of the affected child* | |
| Only child | 11.8 |
| First child | 27.4 |
| Second child | 29.4 |
| Third child | 13.7 |
| Fourth child | 3.9 |
| Fifth child | 5.9 |
| Sixth child | 2.0 |
| Seventh child | 3.9 |
| Unknown | 2.0 |
| (Last child | 35.3) |
| n=50 | |

SCL-90-R instrument (Derogatis, 1983) simultaneously with their parents. The SCL-90-R is a self-report inventory designed to reflect psychological symptom patterns of distress. Only one out of the four reported sufficient psychological stress as indicated by the global severity index to warrant intervention, or caseness. One father and two mothers also reached that level. Individual analysis of the 90 items on the inventory revealed that the four daughters all responded to the following items:

- crying easily;
- difficulty making decisions;
- trouble catching breath;
- frequent arguments;
- shouting or throwing things.

It is noteworthy that these self-reports seem to confirm general parental descriptions of behaviours and the clinical impressions recorded by many professionals. They also suggest a considerable degree of self-awareness.

Comparison of the nine subscales of the SCL-90-R revealed one significant similarity. All four respondents exceeded the minimum cut-off scores for caseness on the subscale of hostility. Further, in each case, hostility was the primary dimension in the individual profile. 'The Hostility dimension reflects thoughts, feelings or actions that are characteristics of the negative affect state of anger. The selection of items includes all three modes of manifestation and reflects qualities such as aggression, irritability, rage and resentment' (Derogatis, 1983). These data are of interest. As all four of the young ladies were living in the family home at the time of testing, we can speculate whether the stress was related to the living environment. On the other hand, it might be related to the age of the respondents, social relationships, the uncertainty of the future, vocational situations, or combinations of these and other factors. More study of stress among PWS subjects is needed.

## HOSPITALIZATIONS

Greenswag (1984a) reported that 82% of her sample (n=228) had been hospitalized for PWS-related problems after age 16. The present study, on the other hand, found that only 61% of subjects (n=23) were hospitalized for PWS-related matters after age 18. The relatively high incidence reported in both studies is noteworthy. Given that persons with PWS may experience a decreased pain sensitivity (Holm, 1981b) and do not have the same response to illness as other persons (e.g., absence of fever, reduced resistance to infection) (Wett, 1985), the former are more likely to be asymptomatic; consequently those working with PWS should be responsive to any expressed or manifest symptoms.

One case brought to the investigator's attention involved an incident of acute bowel obstruction in an 11-year-old girl with PWS (Chapter 2, page 30). Over a period of two days the child mentioned a 'tummy-ache' only a few times and continued with her regular activities, including daily swimming. Although she slept normally and had no fever, she was finally taken to the doctor because her abdomen felt hard and her bowel movements were not formed. She underwent bowel surgery the following day, had intravenous and gastro-intestinal drainage for five days, and returned to school after 12 days. A normal child, according to information given to the mother by the surgeon, would have experienced acute pain, have been physically incapacitated, and taken longer to recover. Similar reports testifying to reduced pain sensitivity for broken bones, dislocated joints, removal of fingernails, dental surgery, and extremes of temperature were supplied by other parents in this study. In a study on surgery and anaesthesia in persons with PWS (n=207), Wett (1985) found a complication rate of 2.5%, a rate he reported to be higher than for the general American population.

These research findings suggest serious implications for preventive health care with PWS. Parents and professionals alike must be cognizant of symptom-detection, and PWS subjects must be taught how to express pain and other symptoms of bodily distress.

## RESIDENTIAL STATUS

At the time of this study, 71% of the PWS children were resident in the family home with at least one of the biological parents. The remaining 29% were in one or other of the following: foster homes (two); boarding home (one); behavioural group home (one); group home for mentally handicapped persons (four); independent flat-living with itinerant support (two); independent flat-living with attendant care (two); and institutional residence (three). The two youngest children residing outside of the family home were 11.8 and 16 years of age, respectively, and both lived in foster situations. All other PWS subjects in alternative residences were over the age of majority.

The prognosis for persons with PWS to live independently during adulthood has in the past been poor. Sulzbacher *et al.* (1981) suggested that 'a group home/sheltered workshop living arrangement can provide maximum happiness and fulfilment for the PWS individual and for the other members of the family'. They admitted, however, that their experience with the young adult population was limited. They briefly described the cases of two persons with PWS who were living independently, one successfully and one against the advice of the authors. The latter situation was characterized by weight gain, unemployment, and interpersonal relationship problems. The Prader–Willi Syndrome Association of America promotes homogeneous group-living situations in 12–15 bed units as cost-effective and programmatically successful (Thompson *et al.*, 1988). Their Medical Alert states that 'adolescents and adults can function well in group living programs if they have adequate calorie control and structured living' ('The Gathered View', 1990b).

Only one subject in the present study was living independently at the time of the survey. This 32-year-old woman received itinerant support from community-living skills workers, but was having difficulties with food control, housekeeping routines, and socialization. Another young lady moved into her own flat subsequent to the study, but unfortunately died from heart failure at the age of 24. In a follow-up to the present study, James and Willott (1989) examined residential options in western Canada and identified ten models providing a range of options with varying degrees of independence (Chapter 7).

A tribute written to Bradley (*PWS Newsletter*, March, 1989) illustrates the dilemma of independent living. As the editor wrote:

> Brad, even as a younger child, always had a powerful determination to be normal, to do the things other kids did, and he was not about to let anyone or anything stop him from trying; he often was successful. And when he was not, he learned from his experience. He had intelligence and spirit everyone admired.

Well, Brad tried, and tried and he succeeded in his ultimate goal of independence.

He died not long ago, shortly after turning 18. But for a time, he really did what he wanted to do – be on his own, have his own home, his own job, the works.

The people who worked with Brad in Winnipeg over the past year learned a tremendous amount from him, not just about the syndrome, but about how to work, and live with someone with the syndrome whom society also recognizes as bright enough and determined enough to live on his own and make his own decisions.

## PRIMARY ACTIVITY

All eligible school-aged PWS children in the present study were attending formal educational programmes at the preschool (16%), primary (52%), or secondary school level (23%). The oldest student still in secondary education was 19 years old and in her graduation year. Eligibility for educational services varied between public and private systems and across jurisdictions. In two districts, PWS students were eligible for secondary education until age 21; in some cases entitlement was only for 12 years of education. In most cases, placements were age-relevant, although many were in the context of ungraded special-education classes. One mainstreamed student was at a grade level two years below his chronological age; others were integrated at grade level. Three toddlers under the age of three years were at home, with varying degrees of itinerant and clinic support. While a few students were functioning in regular education programmes, qualifying comments were added by parents indicating that special-education programmes were attended by some students at all three levels. Recognizing the great variation in special-education support systems across provinces and school jurisdictions, no attempt was made to assess the frequency or degree of educational supports necessary.

Of the adult-age subjects (19–37 years old), 75% attended sheltered workshops or training centres, 5% an institutional programme, and 20% remained at home. Of this last-mentioned group, one female worked at a day-care centre one day a week; the others had no organized primary daily activity. All adult subjects had received at least primary level public education. Two of the oldest members of this group had spent their teenage years in institutions for people with mental handicaps; all the others had received special-education services before ending their formal education.

## SUMMARY

The foregoing discussion of PWS child characteristics has begun to establish a profile of Canadians with this disorder. This chapter examined the results of a Canadian study of children with PWS, making comparisons with a number of non-Canadian studies. In general, the profile is consistent with that documented in the international literature. The reader is referred to Table 1.1 in the first chapter to review characteristic clinical features of PWS. Two additional characteristics noted with high frequency in the current study were a weak or absent cry during infancy, and the presence of axillary and pubic hair in PWS adults. The following observations can be made in summary:

- PWS is increasingly diagnosed between six months and five years of age. It is important to obtain as early a diagnosis as possible, not only for medical reasons but because intervention through early childhood education, whether at home or in preschool programmes, may be critically important in increasing longevity and minimizing the major effects of the disorder.
- Generally, there are few sex differences apparent between males and females in terms of symptomatology. However, it appears there is relatively greater weight gain in males than females over the same age range.
- Extensive weight gain leads to increased mortality; PWS children have had a relatively short life-span compared with non-handicapped persons in the past. It is apparent that there is a trend towards greater longevity, probably associated with improved health management, and possibly because many people are remaining at home rather than

being institutionalized. This would not be inconsistent with evidence in other areas of disability.

- There is also some evidence that cognitive performance declines over age, although care must be taken in interpreting these data because they are cross-sectional rather than longitudinal.
- Since PWS has only recently been recognized as such, there has been a back-log effect surrounding diagnosis. As diagnosis in the past has often not been made until the second or third decades of life, there have been difficulties in providing adequate health care, education, and general planning for those with the syndrome. The problems associated with less-than-optimal care can also lead to reduced cognitive functioning and greater mortality.
- With earlier diagnosis, improved health care, and better understanding of home, community, and educational management, longevity will be increased and performance enhanced. Although there is at present no 'cure' for the condition, improvement in a multiplicity of areas will ameliorate at least some of its effects.
- It has been noted above that educational problems arise out of the social and health aspects of PWS. These can restrict educational opportunities, yet studies concerning problems in poor self-care, eating, and social skills, using tests such as the PAC, indicate that appropriate remedial education is possible and urgent.
- The results show great variability in social, cognitive, and allied areas. There is no direct or simple educational response to PWS children, but, as in other learning situations, the development of individual programme-planning allied to links between assessment and intervention are critical.
- The need for a holistic approach by professionals working together is clearly identified. The need for early intervention and home support from skilled practitioners appears to be a major gap.

# Chapter 5

# Canadian PWS-parent profile

In addition to establishing the profile of Canadian PWS children, James (1987) gathered demographic data on the PWS-parent population. This chapter presents a PWS-parent profile in the context of current literature. Of particular importance is the discussion related to PWS parental stress. As many parents testify, the 24-hour supervision requirements over a prolonged period produces a great deal of personal and familial stress. A comparison of parental stress to that of other population groups, and an examination of stress in relation to parent needs and PWS child welfare concerns is included.

## MARITAL STATUS

In 47% of the cases, the PWS child was living with the biological, married parents. Another 14% of the PWS children lived with a biological parent and a new spouse or partner (i.e., remarried or cohabiting); 10% were living with the mother only. Table 5.1 provides data on the marital status of the natural parent(s) for PWS children living at home and elsewhere. No attempt was made to follow up on the status of marriage partners who had left the family home.

The number of parents in the family (Beckman, 1983), family sharing (Byrne and Cunningham, 1987), the degree of marital satisfaction (Friedrich, 1979; Friedrich *et al.*, 1985), maternal depression, locus of control, and the family social climate (Friedrich *et al.*, 1985) have all been found to be significant factors in parental coping in families with a disabled child. Broken marriages, therefore, can reasonably be expected to tax coping resources. Of the 20 PWS subjects in this study who were not

**Table 5.1** Marital status of natural PWS parent(s)

| | *Child at home* | | *Child elsewhere* | | *Total* | |
|---|---|---|---|---|---|---|
| | *Freq* | % | *Freq* | % | *Freq* | % |
| Married | 24 | 47.1 | 5 | 9.8 | 29 | 56.9 |
| Remarried | 4 | 7.8 | 3 | 5.9 | 7 | 13.7 |
| Cohabiting | 3 | 5.9 | 0 | 0.0 | 3 | 5.9 |
| Separated | 2 | 3.9 | 0 | 0.0 | 2 | 3.9 |
| Divorced | 1 | 2.0 | 0 | 0.0 | 1 | 2.0 |
| Widowed | 2 | 3.9 | 2 | 3.9 | 4 | 7.8 |
| Unknown* | 0 | 0.0 | 5 | 9.8 | 5 | 9.8 |
| Total | 36 | 70.6 | 15 | 29.4 | 51 | 100 |

* *Includes* foster placement (1), group home placements (2), unreported (2).

residing with both natural parents, only one child remained with the natural father. The effect of the marital situation may well be an important factor, therefore, in maternal stress.

Conversely, the severity of concerns associated with PWS suggests the likelihood of increased pressures on marital relationships. Friedrich *et al.* (1985) found that the severity of the disability and the degree of behaviour problems are both directly related to familial problems. The figure for intact marriages of the biological parents (56.9%) suggests that marital breakdown may be a concern in PWS families. While several mothers acknowledged the inability of the departed spouse to cope with the needs of the PWS child, only a few admitted that the presence of the PWS child contributed to the marital breakdown.

## PARENTAL AGE AT CHILDBIRTH

Maternal age at the birth of the PWS child was available in 40 cases. Figure 5.1 presents a summary of birthing age by five-year maternal age bands. Specific ages in six additional cases were undeterminable, but all would likely fall below age 30, hence contributing to slight increases in the first three age groupings. Seventy-four percent of the children for whom data were available were born before the mother reached age 30;

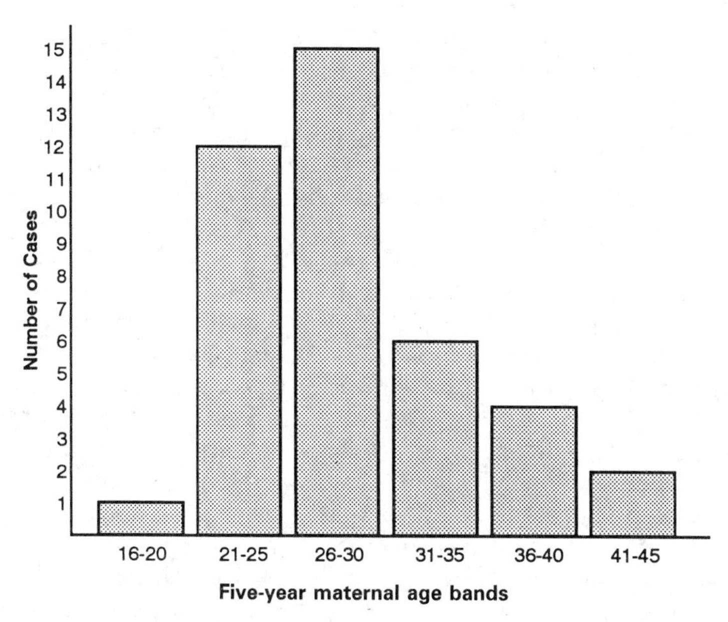


**Figure 5.1** Maternal age at childbirth by five-year age bands.

96% were born before maternal age 40. At the time of childbirth, 61% of the fathers were under the age of 30, and 96% were under age 40 (n=28).

There does not appear to be a maternal-age relationship with the incidence of PWS, as has long been known with Down's syndrome. The PWS peak maternal quinquennial age at childbirth in the present study (26–30) is similar to Thuline's figures for the general American population, and is consistent with provincial (Province of Alberta, 1984) and national statistics (Government of Canada, 1981) for the general Canadian population. While the mean age at childbirth for Down's syndrome mothers, used as a comparison group in the present study, was lower than in Thuline's study, it was still significantly higher than for the PWS mothers.

The ages in this study are similar to those reported in various other PWS studies (Butler *et al.*, 1986; Dunn *et al.*, 1981). It should be noted, however, that Greenswag (1984a) found over one-half of the mothers in her study to be over the age of 30, and 15% over the age of 40. By contrast only 26% in the present survey were over age 30 and 4% over age 40. Earlier, Dunn (1968) had found a mean maternal age of 33.6 years in a small series (n=9) of Canadian PWS mothers, which was acknowledged to be higher than contemporary literature reports, but left unexplained. In a later study Dunn *et al.* (1981) found no age difference of significance between PWS mothers and general population mothers (n=23). The present study is in keeping with this finding.

Dunn (1968) reported the mean paternal age of 18 international PWS cases to be 29.2 years (22–40 years) and nine Canadian cases to be 35 years (27–45 years). The mean paternal age for all the cases was 31.1 years. Later work by the same author (Dunn *et al.*, 1981) found a mean paternal age of 30.9 years (n=21), a figure slightly, but not significantly, higher than for the general population in Canada. The present study found 61% of the fathers to be under age 30 (mean 27.8; range 20–39) and 100% to be under age 40 at the time of the birth of their PWS child. Mean paternal age in this study is only marginally lower than in other studies, and consonant with general population figures.

## NUMBER OF CHILDREN

The number of children born to PWS parents ranged from one to seven. At the time of this study, however, there were no more than four children residing within any family home (Table 4.4, p. 80). In six instances (12%) parents had no more children when their first child had PWS; in 18 other cases (35%), with two or more children they ceased child bearing after the birth of their PWS child.

In comparison to families in Greenswag's (1984a) study, the western Canadian families were smaller. The mean number of children in the present investigation was 3.04, compared to 3.9 reported by Greenswag (1984a). Seventy percent of the families in the present study had three or fewer children, while only 48% of Greenswag's families had three or less. Further, families in the latter research ranged to 16 siblings, whereas the largest family in the present study had only seven children. As Greenswag's participants were almost exclusively from the United

States, it may be that there are national differences evident in these figures; the smaller numbers may also be a reflection of a decline in family size in recent years.

## STRESS

The SCL-90-R (Derogatis, 1983), a self-measure of psychopathological aspects of stress, was administered across three groups of parents in this study: Prader–Willi syndrome (PWS), Down's syndrome (DS), and non-handicapped (NH). The SCL-90-R yields nine subscale dimensions of stress and three global indices. The results were compared by groups and by sex, and the global severity index for stress correlated to demographics, parental concerns, and intervention strategies.

### Mothers

Differences of significance on four female subscales and one male subscale were noted. As a group, PWS mothers scored higher on the obsessive-compulsive, interpersonal sensitivity, and psychoticism subscales when compared to the mothers of non-handicapped children.

The obsessive-compulsive scale focuses on repetitive thoughts, impulses, or actions that are of an unwanted nature. During interviews, mothers described compulsive behaviours such as maintaining a spotless kitchen, or checking and double-checking what had been done. They also admitted to obsessive, and often unpleasant, thoughts relating to family members. Frustrations associated with the constant caring for the PWS child would make them want to lash out physically, to yell, to hide, or to run away, all of which they described as irrational reactions to situations. The interpersonal sensitivity reflects personal feelings of inferiority and inadequacy. Some mothers made self-deprecating comments and described feelings of uneasiness in social situations, which are consistent with high scores on this scale. It is not unusual for a mother to feel acutely self-conscious in interpersonal interactions, particularly with a PWS dependant present.

The psychoticism scale provides a continuum from mild interpersonal alienation to evidence of psychosis. Illustrative of this scale would be the mothers who described periods of withdrawal and isolation, or who admitted to having feelings that were not their own, or to carrying the burden of punishment for their sins. While individual NH mothers may have shown elevated scores on any one or more of these same scales, as a group they scored significantly lower than the PWS mothers, suggesting that the stresses associated with parenting NH children do not occur to the same degree.

### Fathers

Somatization, the only male subscale of significance, reflects distress resulting from perceptions of bodily dysfunction. The results suggest that PWS fathers are more likely to complain about cardiovascular, gastro-intestinal or respiratory problems than their spouses. The chances seem greater that they will experience headaches, backaches, weakness, and other somatic signs of anxiety. Such symptoms have a high prevalence in disorders with a functional aetiology, that is of non-organic causation. It may be that fathers consciously or unconsciously use somatic complaints as a means of getting attention from their spouses in competition with their special-needs children. On the other hand, because there were no differences of significance across the three groups, one might conclude that fathers in general are more likely to display a somatic reaction to stress than their spouses.

The similarly high-stress levels between PWS spouses provides evidence of the need for parental supprts. Preventive intervention is needed to preserve the integrity of the family unit and the mental health of parents. Despite the large number of parents in this study who reached the definition of a diagnosed case according to the decision rule for the SCL-90-R, very few were actually receiving assistance. For most there was a personal awareness of their own stress level. There was also an acceptance of stress as a way of life that was not changeable.

### Comparison with other groups

The SCL-90-R decision rule for caseness, that is to say the score that serves to define a case needing intervention, was applied across all three groups, with results shown in Table 5.2. It is notable that mothers of PWS and DS children recorded similar levels of distress when compared to mothers of NH children. For mothers, traditionally the primary parent in child-rearing, the demands of caring for children with either of these syndromes results in similar levels of global indices of distress. On the other hand, the distress levels of PWS fathers was about double that of DS fathers. Which factors contribute to this difference is uncertain, although it is speculated that adjustments in family eating patterns, and the need for paternal involvement in child supervision may be relevant.

**Table 5.2** Caseness of SCL-90-R respondents by group and sex

| *Sex* | *PWS* | *DS* | *NH* |
|---|---|---|---|
| Female | 16/29<br>(55.17%) | 11/21<br>(52.38%) | 6/30<br>(20%) |
| Male | 9/19<br>(47.36%) | 4/17<br>(25.53%) | 2/18<br>(11.11%) |
| Family mean | 25/48<br>(52.08%) | 15/38<br>(39.47%) | 8/48<br>(16.66%) |

The relative similarity of stress levels between the PWS parents is also of interest. Given that 39% of the families involved separation of the biological parents, and that only one of the PWS children was living with the natural father, it is suspected that the 47% caseness of PWS fathers reported in Table 5.2 may represent an underestimate of PWS paternal stress levels; stress levels of PWS fathers who left the marriage relationship may have been significantly higher than for those remaining in the relationship.

It is suggested that PWS parents as a group are about 30 years behind the DS parents in their advocacy for awareness and services. Much has occurred in the last few decades in public education regarding DS, and there now are many supports for families. The formation of the Canadian Down's Syndrome Society, for example, has created a national profile, and facilitated conferences, newsletters, and networking. The prognosis for health, education, and welfare in general is relatively well understood by professionals in most disciplines. Hence DS parents are not likely to be stressed to the same degree by the drain of public education and advocacy that many PWS parents now face.

These data on parental stress indicate a need, and suggest the direction, for intervention programmes to maintain the mental health of parents, and the integrity of marriages and parent/child relationships.

## EMPLOYMENT

Approximately 40% of the PWS mothers were employed or involved in educational activities outside of the home; 47% identified themselves as housewives. Approximately 70% of the fathers who were in the family home were employed, with another 10% having reached retirement status.

Similar numbers of PWS and DS mothers remained at home as housewives, while slightly more of the NH mothers went to work. There were great variations in family circumstances, however, which contributed to whether or not the mother worked. Having older siblings available to care for a school-aged PWS child before and after school hours, for example, allowed one mother to maintain her full-time professional position; by contrast, single parents more often worked at part-time or shift employment, allowing flexibility in covering child-supervision requirements. This latter observation is consistent with the findings of Watson and Midlarsky (1979). The care requirements of PWS children were most frequently cited as a reason for mothers not working.

## EDUCATION

Educational levels for parents ranged from less than secondary school graduation to university graduation for each sex.

Adjusted frequency percentages indicate somewhat similar profiles by sex, i.e., 30% of females (n=30) and 36% of males (n=22) had less than grade 12 education, 37% of females and 32% of males completed secondary school graduation or apprenticeship qualifications, 20% of females and 9% of males completed from one to three years of college, and 13% of females and 23% of males had a university degree or equivalent professional training. At the tertiary level mothers tended to have shorter training programmes and less professional status than fathers.

Byrne and Cunningham (1987) indicated educational level to be a predictor variable significantly correlated to stress in families with Down's syndrome children, with lower stress in families where both parents had further education. Of the 25 individual PWS cases reaching a sufficient level of measurable stress to warrant intervention, 17 (68%) had grade 12 or less education; only two (4%) had a university degree. Hence stress, as measured by caseness on the SCL-90-R, also seems to be associated with less education. Interestingly, both individuals with university degrees had inordinate stresses to cope with beyond PWS. In one case, the PWS child had a degenerative kidney condition and was exhibiting considerable school problems; in the other, a second child had required surgery for a congenital heart condition, and marital separation had occurred. By contrast, of the eight NH cases which reached the same level of caseness, only two (25%) had grade 12 or less education, and six (75%) had some tertiary training, including two with university degrees.

While stress in PWS families seems higher among parents with less than secondary school graduation, stress in the NH families seems to be more common where parents have pursued tertiary education or training. This observation, however, is based on a very small sample. In terms of PWS-parent intervention, it seems that less-educated parents require more particular targetting.

## CONCERNS FOR THE PWS CHILD

Parents' responses to concerns for the welfare of their children are summarized in Table 5.3. Items are presented in descending order of concern according to mean scores. Independence, social relationships, and health issues were consistently the parents' biggest concerns; the lack of sexual development, on the other hand, caused the least concern.

**Table 5.3** PWS parental child welfare concerns

| | *Mean* |
|---|---|
| Independence | 1.79 |
| Social relationships | 1.83 |
| Health | 1.87 |
| Occupational training | 2.06 |
| Self-esteem | 2.15 |
| Alternate residential options | 2.15 |
| Sexual development | 2.62 |
| n=47 | |

Parents responding to the opportunity to add 'other' concerns cited education and uncertainty of the future as issues. Both of these also were raised by many parents during the interviews.

Correlation coefficients were determined for the seven child welfare concerns listed in Table 5.3 and the SCL-90-R global severity index (GSI) scores by gender. Only the correlation of the male GSI score and the concern for social relationships reached a level of statistical significance, suggesting that fathers as a group experience some stress related to the social relationships of their PWS child.

In examining the correlations between the child welfare concerns and the list of specific interventions, one concern had more frequent significant correlations with interventions attempted, namely, the concern for alternate residential options. When considering the frequency of significant correlations between the parental child welfare concern items and the frequency of interventions attempted by age group, only one concern was most specifically associated with one age group. Parental concern for the sexual development of their child was most often correlated to the frequency of attempted interventions in the 6 to 12-year-old age grouping.

## NEEDS

Parents were asked to respond to six items of parental needs. The mean results in order of descending importance are presented in Table 5.4.

**Table 5.4** Parental needs

| | *Mean* |
|---|---|
| Behaviour-management strategies | 2.11 |
| More medical information | 2.23 |
| Diet and nutrition assistance | 2.36 |
| Peer-support group | 2.60 |
| Respite care | 3.02 |
| Personal-stress counselling | 3.17 |
| n=47 | |

Two concerns had a considerable number of significant correlations with specific interventions attempted: the concern for a peer-support group and the concern for respite care had more than four times as many significant correlations as any other parent-need items. Both of these were most evident during the teenage and adult years.

The matter of parental peer-support deserves a comment. Parents were often split on the value of involvement in PWS parent associations (Chapter 8), yet few were able to cite effective peer-support groups other than such associations. In the absence of professional supports, as criticized by parents, there seems to be a need for parents to improve their services to each other. It is recognized, however, that this is difficult in a largely rural geographic area like western Canada.

## CONCERNS AND CHILD BEHAVIOUR

Parental concerns for specific child behaviours are ranked in descending order of concern, according to mean scores, in Table 5.5. This list reflects a general level of concern without consideration of age or sex. Stubbornness, gorging, peer conflict, tantrums, and manipulation topped the list of parental concerns regarding their child's behaviour. Conflict with external authority, tantrums, and gullibility were significantly correlated with mothers' GSI scores. Given that mothers handle most of the interactions with external authorities, such as education and social services, and must manage the behaviour of the PWS child more than their spouses, it is understandable that these items would be related to their stress levels. Mothers too are more likely to be concerned for the interpersonal interactions of their child, and hence be more aware of the child's gullibility.

**Table 5.5** Parental child behaviour concerns

| | *Mean* |
|---|---|
| Stubbornness | 2.02 |
| Gorging | 2.28 |
| Peer conflict | 2.39 |
| Tantrums | 2.41 |
| Manipulation | 2.41 |
| Parent conflict | 2.67 |
| Defiance | 2.76 |
| External authority conflict | 2.94 |
| Sibling conflict | 2.95 |
| Gullibility | 2.98 |
| Somnolence | 3.09 |
| Wandering | 3.50 |

The concerns with gullibility and tantrums were most frequently correlated with specific interventions attempted. Additionally, several trends were evident. Tantrums, gullibility, wandering, and defiance were most often correlated with the frequency of interventions attempted in the birth-to-five-year age-grouping; a concern for somnolence was most frequently correlated with the 6–12-year age group; and the four concerns relating to conflict – with siblings, peers, parents, and external authority – were almost exclusively related to the frequency of correlations with interventions attempted with the teenagers and adults. The concerns with parent conflict and with sibling conflict were more often correlated with the frequency of interventions attempted over the age of 19 years.

Understanding the relationship of child behaviours to parental stress should be helpful in addressing the content of parent-support programmes. To date, counsellors have relied upon parent identification of stressful areas; now there is some objective support for areas to be addressed.

## SUMMARY

Chapter 5 presented a profile of Canadian PWS parents with references to the international literature.

- There appears to be no association between the age of the mother or father and the birth of a PWS child.
- Mothers and fathers of PWS children tend to show particular personality reactions to high stress. In comparison with mothers of non-handicapped children, mothers of PWS children tend to display obsessive-compulsive behaviour, sensitivity to interpersonal relationships and alienation. There were more frequent signs of obsessional behaviour than among mothers without PWS children. PWS mothers often had aggressive thoughts about the family, and felt inadequate, inferior, and self-conscious about their situation and behaviour. They also often felt withdrawn or isolated, and some had feelings of being punished.
- Fathers of PWS children, on the other hand, tended to show stress reactions in terms of bodily dysfunction. They perceived themselves as having greater cardiovascular, gastrointestinal and respiratory problems, compared with other fathers. Symptoms such as backache and headache also were more common.
- It is important for families to obtain help before stress builds up, and the support needs to be ongoing. Parents require

knowledge about stress reactions as soon as they have a PWS child, and need to know about mechanisms for coping with possible reactions. Social services departments need to be sensitive to these concerns, as do other professionals who work with such families. The types of help required should be available on a flexible basis to meet individual family needs.

- PWS mothers are more likely to remain in the house than mothers of normal children. This is probably a reaction to the child's eating behaviours, stubbornness and tantrums. It may also be a cause as well as a reaction to stress.
- Just as children with PWS show a wide range of variability, so do their parents. It would be inappropriate to make generalizations about parental behaviour, stress, or intervention based on a study of this size, although significant trends do emerge.
- The education levels of parents crosses all social groups, and there is some evidence to suggest that those with a higher level of education suffer less stress. This may be a reflection of ability or adaptive skill, possibly associated with an ability to control stress, or to find compensations and outlets.
- Parents indicate they want information about: implementing behaviour-management strategies; comprehensive medical information; diet and nutrition; opportunity for peer support; recognizing and coping with personal stress; and the availability of respite care.
- Parental concerns relate to children showing: stubbornness; gorging; conflicts with peers; temper tantrums; and manipulation. Other issues include children's manipulating parents into conflict, defiance by the child, and problems with external authority. Also listed are gullibility, somnolence, and wandering behaviour. It is apparent that the manipulative and externally directed behaviours are those for which parents require the greatest help. Yet for some parents other areas of behaviour may require equal attention because of their implications for child development.

*Chapter 6*

# Intervention strategies

Chapter 6 presents a discussion of home and community interventions surveyed by James (1987). The PWS literature on intervention strategies to date originated largely in clinical settings; there appears to be little documented evidence of which home interventions or community supports parents of PWS children find effective, beyond parental testimony in parent-support materials. This chapter looks at what helps PWS parents as a group to cope.

Due to the daily supervision requirements and the prolonged burden of caring, parents and their PWS children may share a closeness beyond that shared by families with non-handicapped children. As well, professionals often rely heavily on parents for the implementation of dietary, medical, behavioural, and social interventions, thus leaving the parents with the major responsibility for structuring and monitoring most daily activities of their PWS children in the home and community.

To explore what parents perceive as being effective intervention is important because parental perceptions can assist professionals in coping more effectively with prognostic quality-of-life issues, which in the past have been so uncertain and today are of increasing concern.

The question this study has tried to address is, how effective are these interventions for assisting the family in the home and in the community? Often parents learn to cope in spite of professional assistance. This may be particularly true for PWS parents, given there is so little documentation from which to learn. Professionals must learn from the real experts – the parents – for as Leconte (1981) states, many PWS parents 'have developed techniques of management that may or may not be related to theory, but that are often very effective'.

The study by James (1987) explored several research questions relating to interventions. Parents were asked to assess 64 interventions taken from the literature and from the clinical experience of the author. The developmental stage at which the intervention occurred was identified, and each intervention was rated according to its efficacy. The 64 items were grouped according to eight domains: medical, dietary, allied health, environmental, behavioural, developmental, social, parental. (See Appendix B for a complete list of interventions surveyed.)

The following discussion summarizes the results of the interventions surveyed under two broad categories: effective home supports and effective community-based supports. The two are not mutually exclusive; rather, there is considerable overlap. Most community supports, for example, cannot take place without parents providing transportation to and from appointments, implementing recommendations in the home, or monitoring some aspect of programming. Within these categories, discussion focuses on interventions by domain. A section on family coping, outlining some of the major ways in which families and individuals adapt to a PWS family member, concludes the chapter.

## EFFECTIVE CONTROLS: HOME-BASED

Home-based interventions are procedures for which parents have primary responsibility in terms of initiating and supervising.

### Environmental interventions

Keeping the kitchen counters always cleared was considered an effective environmental control. This was not surprising as parent literature advocates clearing food away promptly after a meal and washing the dishes or putting them in an inaccessible place (Pipes, 1981). However, more than one-half of the parents said they had not tried this preventive measure. The importance of such routine housekeeping should not be overlooked; habit often becomes as important for other family members as it does for the affected individual.

Seven of the eight environmental interventions had not been tried by 55–90% of parents. The low response to these items may in part be due to the fact that several interventions are oriented to the older PWS subject: for example, controls on spending money and supervision while shopping would not be applicable to preschoolers, or possibly even primary age children. On the other hand, although parent literature (e.g., Pipes, 1981; Tomaseski-Heinemann, 1988; Thompson, 1986) advocates the use of locks on kitchens, cupboards, refrigerators, and freezers, four of five households had never tried such measures. According to the medical alert published by the Prader–Willi Syndrome Association of America, locked food control is essential ('The Gathered View', 1990b). This may be simply because parents have not had access to literature or information of this type. As only 42% of the respondents replied that they found PWS parent-group participation to be moderately or very effective, it is possible that the majority of parents do not avail themselves of the resources existing through parent associations.

In terms of effectiveness based on the adjusted frequency percentages, that is based on the number actually trying the intervention, the environmental domain was the only one in which all listed interventions were considered to be highly effective (78–100%). Low-incidence interventions, such as locks on kitchen entry doors and food cupboards, are considered to be highly effective. This underscores again the need to inform parents of possible interventions.

## Behavioural interventions

Three behavioural interventions were considered to be effective: praise, isolation, and deprivation of privileges. Praise was perceived to be the most effective intervention of those surveyed (66% of respondents). PWS child response to praise has been noted elsewhere in the literature (Neason, 1978). Anecdotal comments by parents affirm a basic behavioural principle: behaviours that are praised tend to occur more often.

Isolation, as practised by the parents in this study, usually referred to time-out in the child's bedroom. There were, however, a few reports of isolation equating to confinement, that is to say in a locked room. Isolation was most often terminated by the child; duration was often short, although in PWS adults a period of sleep often followed confinement or isolation. Parents frequently reported positive changes in behaviour when using the isolation procedure, although 27% of the parents rated the procedure as moderately or very ineffective. This was the only intervention that had a substantial number of polarized views.

Integral to the efficacy of isolation or time out seemed to be placement in a familiar surrounding (usually the child's bedroom); removal of all sources of food stimuli; and open-ended permission to return, contingent upon appropriate behaviour. Parents citing this procedure as ineffective largely had non-compliant children who had to be forcibly directed to isolation, and who became retaliatory and destructive. Thus, the procedure may or may not be appropriate for individual situations.

The third successful behavioural intervention, deprivation of privileges, should be understood in terms of a temporary withholding of privileges rather than long-term deprivation. Parent comments suggest that the consequence of bad behaviour (deprivation) must be established in advance and meted out with consistency. Privileges referred to were non-food items which could be used as reinforcers of desired behaviours, e.g., television, special outings, and favourite purchases.

Despite the popular support for these three behavioural interventions, only praise was considered to be highly effective when viewed in terms of the adjusted frequency percentages (82%). The fact that only one out of nine listed behavioural interventions was seen as highly effective suggests that while such interventions may frequently be attempted, they meet with only a modicum of success. In fact, two such interventions – deprivation of food and physical punishment – were considered to be ineffective based on adjusted frequency percentages. The trial use of various options is important as some interventions may be appropriate for one child and not for another.

When compared across domains, the behavioural domain was of the greatest use to the parents, yet the need for behaviour-management strategies was still identified by the parents (Table 5.4, p.97) as the pre-eminent need. As pointed out in the literature review, while behavioural interventions hold much promise in working with PWS, there is not a well-documented literature as yet in this area. Given the present stature of behavioural psychology, this area is the logical one in which to attempt gains in working with PWS in the future.

### Parental interventions

Participation in a PWS parent association was cited second only to praise as an effective support. Only 12% judged such association to be moderately or very ineffective. However, 33% of the respondents claimed they had not tried parent-group involvement. A major problem is geography. In rural areas, PWS families often are isolated, without opportunity for contact with other such families. Through their newsletters, parent associations have been the only supportive link for some of these families. Some urban parents admitted, however, that while the local association was doing some essential work, they personally did not attend meetings because they were not interested in hearing about other people's problems unrelated to their own. Unfortunately, since all support groups in western Canada are very small, it will be difficult to meet everyone's needs. This issue was addressed by Brooks-Bertrum and Mitchell (1986) when they pointed out that there are three distinct sets of parents with needs: those with very young children; those with adolescents; and those with ageing children.

The other two effective parent-orientated interventions involved baby-sitting support. Family baby-sitting was favoured only slightly above private baby-sitting. Arguments in favour of using relatives included convenience, eagerness of the relative to assist, and a meaningful relationship with the child. On the other hand, negative comments centred on an over-indulgent attitude (particularly of grandparents) and non-adherence to dietary controls and behaviour-management principles; the inability of the relative to provide the necessary supervision due to advancing age and decreasing energy levels; and the lack of availability of relatives due to distance. Private baby-sitting was more straightforward. There were many descriptions of why sitters were never called a second time, usually related to a lack of control of the child. The problems associated with getting a reliable sitter dissuaded some parents from participating in some social activities.

In addition to the three items already mentioned, two additional low-incidence interventions – respite care (82%) and stress counselling (100%) – were judged to be highly effective when considered by adjusted frequency percentages. Thus five out of the eight parent supports ranged from 76–100% effective. The latter score was given by nine parents who had received stress counselling. At the other extreme, however, were co-operative baby-sitting (100%) and marriage counselling (100%). The few families who attempted these interventions considered them to be very ineffective.

## EFFECTIVE CONTROLS: COMMUNITY-BASED

Community controls are those that originate and occur primarily outside the place of residence, and rely on the expertise of professionals to implement.

### Medical interventions

Only regular monitoring by a specialist was generally perceived to be an effective medical intervention. Specialists most often cited were paediatricians and endocrinologists. While 21 (50%) of the 42 respondents affirmed specialists, and 11 (26%) found regular monitoring by a GP to be effective, there were 12 (29%) respondents who found medical monitoring by a GP to be ineffective. Medical doctors were more often criticized by parents than were any other professionals during the interviews. Drotar's (1981) view that the physical care of chronically ill children takes place in a highly charged interpersonal arena seems to apply to PWS. Consistent with literature reports relating to chronic disability (Drotar, 1981; Doernberg, 1982), parents tend to ascribe more skills and knowledge to medical doctors than they may possess, failing to recognize the limits of their training, which results in personal frustrations. Criticisms centred on the pursuit of the diagnosis, the manner in which the diagnosis was given, and support to the family after diagnosis.

The perceived ambivalence of some doctors, the number

seen, the advocacy role required of the parents, and the extended time in obtaining a diagnosis all contribute to parental discontent. Many parents related personal trauma as a result of the manner in which the diagnosis was ultimately received. Some were given the diagnosis over the telephone with litle explanation; others were shown pictures of grossly obese individuals, given a poor prognosis, and advised not to take the infant home; some women were given the diagnosis without the support of the husband present; and many were given a varying series of tentative and possible diagnoses, which only heightened the stress. A common complaint was the lack of information for the layman.

The inability of the medical profession to extend meaningful, ongoing support to the family was also upsetting to many. Angered by previous experiences, some parents claimed to avoid seeing doctors 'unless absolutely essential'. Like the subjects of Kornblatt and Heinrich (1985), these parents were psychologically predisposed to wait for a crisis before seeking help.

Under such circumstances, concern must be expressed for the health and welfare of the PWS child. Given the implications of the reduced sensitivity to pain (Holm, 1981b) and the abnormal response to illness (Wett, 1985) discussed earlier, PWS children need the assurance of optimal medical attention. Medical doctors must become better informed about PWS, including psycho-social implications for the family; correspondingly, parents must be educated to understand the scope and limitations of all professional supports available to them.

## Dietary interventions

Although this domain contained a combination of home- and community-based interventions, it is reported here because the only two interventions of consequence were both community-based. The only dietary intervention rated as effective was consultation with a nutritionist or a dietitian, yet the adjusted frequency percentage was only a moderately effective 63% (17 out of 27 respondents). Thus none of the dietary interventions listed was considered to be highly effective. One low-incidence resource used – participation in a self-help weight-control group such as Weight-Watchers – was judged to be ineffective by 50% (n=4).

The absence of highly effective interventions is of concern. As dietary management is the primary requisite in families with PWS children, there appears to be a critical gap in this area. Almost one-half of the comments supplied by parents indicated that they simply give 'smaller, regular portions'.

## Allied health interventions

Allied health professionals usually are seen for secondary problems associated with PWS. Ophthalmology was considered to be effective, reflecting the high frequency of strabismus found in PWS (Bray *et al.*, 1983; Holm, 1981a). In terms of adjusted frequency percentages, ophthalmologists (91%), orthodontists (88%), and chiropractors (80%) were all rated highly, although the last mentioned was based on very small numbers.

These professionals can make important contributions to the quality of life of individuals with PWS, however, there are two primary issues with respect to allied health interventions: awareness and accessibility. More parental awareness of the allied health services available and the possible benefits for their child is needed. Nowak (1988) points out, for example, that there are compromising conditions and limitations that increase the risk of dental disease with PWS, yet parents in the present study were not generally aware of issues in this allied health area. (It should be noted that local and provincial dental associations usually have lists of dentists knowledgeable about working with patients and handicapping conditions, which can be helpful in obtaining appropriate service.)

The costs associated with some professional services are not covered under provincial medical schemes in Canada. Not everyone has equal access, for example, to additional dental insurance plans or extended health-care benefits. There is an absence of PWS literature from allied health professionals, probably reflecting a lack of experience by these practitioners with PWS.

## Developmental interventions

Special-education classes were generally considered to be effective at all levels of the school system. Twenty-five out of the thirty (83%) families responding considered special-education programmes to be effective. All adults in this study, and most of the school-aged children, had received some special-education assistance. Special-education classes are variously understood as classes for children with mental handicaps, learning disabilities, or behavioural disturbance in most areas. With integration, some PWS pupils have remained in regular classrooms with varying degrees of support, e.g., aide time, speech and language therapy, or extra help in a resource room or learning-assistance centre.

School-related concerns raised by parents frequently centred around appropriateness of placement, behavioural management at school, food control while at school, and food control to and from school.

Continued emphasis on integration may result in fewer segregated classroom placements in the future. The success of integration for PWS students will be dependent on successful behavioural-management strategies, and the appropriateness of instructional methodologies. Sulzbacher *et al.* (1981) pointed out that the school curriculum at the primary level need not be much different than for other learning disabled children. Yet many of the PWS students in western Canada are labelled by educators as mentally handicapped. According to the parents, the school difficulties become particularly stressful at the junior secondary level, where the effects of streaming, rotating classrooms, and multiple teachers interact with immature adolescent development, behavioural aberrations, and exposure to the community at large. This latter point is of considerable concern, for as PWS children leave smaller neighbourhood primary schools and move into larger, centralized secondary schools, they are presented with expanding sources of food temptation, both in school and in transit.

Speech and language services were judged by 17 out of 20 (85%) parents in this study to be effective, and were almost exclusively delivered to school-aged children in educational settings. Such services were not uniformly available across all jurisdictions. In a study of 21 PWS youngsters, Branson (1981) did not find enough common elements related to speech and language problems to generalize particular treatment strategies to all her subjects. Therapy, therefore, seems to be as individualized as perhaps the opportunity to receive it.

Swimming was also considered to be effective by parents (76%), although it was not always evaluated from a developmental perspective. Swimming was the most commonly cited recreational activity overall, and was mentioned regularly for adults. It appears that what is begun as a developmental activity in terms of structured handicapped swim programmes (25 out of 42 respondents), translates for many into a lifetime leisure activity. Four teenagers and adults further found reward in the competitive aspects of swimming through the Special Olympics programme, or a similar organization.

Infant stimulation (80%) and music therapy (83%) were less frequently attempted interventions, but given high effectiveness ratings when considered by the adjusted frequency percentages. Infant stimulation programmes are more common today than in the past, but accessibility is still an issue in some places.

Music therapy, on the other hand, is not commonly available, but may hold considerable potential for working with PWS. Several parents commented on the musical interests of their child. For many of the teenagers and adults, listening to music was a recreational pursuit. Phonograph records, in fact, were used as motivators on some occasions. It was evident that music was not just a passive interest for some individuals with PWS: one adult male entertained the investigator with several a cappella renditions of contemporary gospel songs; another adult male was described as having been a soloist in his church. Neither was formally trained. The academic nature of formal music study may deter parents from considering lessons for their child, but the experiential approach to music as a therapy may hold great rewards and therapeutic potential.

## Social interventions

The psycho-social nature of PWS has been emphasized by several writers (Greenswag, 1984a; Hermann, 1981; Neason, 1978), and there is a need for opportunities and structured interventions in this area. Integrated participation in regular youth groups was considered effective by 22 out of 26 (85%) families responding to this item. Groups cited included church youth, day-care, bowling, track and field, and aerobics.

Integration into regular groups was noted by parents as being easier for children up to age 12; social and physical differences by the teenage years makes it difficult to integrate. Indeed, Leconte (1981) suggests that behaviour-management problems in the teenage years may make it impossible for many recreational programmes to accept a child with PWS. Parmenter (1988) has pointed out the need to explore how the environment reacts to people with disabilities, particularly the degree to which personal and social integration is encouraged. It is the hope of many younger parents that as society changes and accepts the variability of handicapping conditions a wider range of discrepancies can be absorbed, making integration of those with PWS easier. The PWS children of today will hopefully find more acceptance among the adults of tomorrow.

While regular youth-group participation is upheld by some parents as desirable, participation in special programmes has been effective for others. Two activities rated highly as adjusted frequency percentages were handicap summer camp programmes (84%) and competitive sports (83%), such as Special Olympics. Several teenagers and adults had been very successful in the latter, and proudly displayed their medals and ribbons to the investigator. While integration is an ideal, parents must be wary of preventing meaningful social activity and training from taking place through specialized programmes.

## SUMMARY

This chapter has examined a variety of intervention methods that have proved useful for some parents. Interventions frequently utilized with successful results are summarized in Table 6.1; others used less frequently, but considered to be highly effective, are listed in Table 6.2. While it is apparent that there are certain behavioural strategies which are helpful, there is a wide range of behaviour that needs to be modified, and the susceptibility of that behaviour to change varies among

**Table 6.1** Interventions with high-frequency and high-effectiveness ratings

| *Domain* | *Intervention* | *% of total sample* | *Effectiveness (%)* |
|---|---|---|---|
| Medical | Monitoring by a specialist | 50 | 63 |
| Dietary | Nutritionist/dietitian consultation | 41 | 63 |
| Allied health | Ophthalmology | 45 | 90 |
| Environmental | Kitchen counters cleared | 42 | 86 |
| Behavioural | Deprivation of privileges | 47 | 74 |
| | Isolation | 40 | 61 |
| | Praise | 64 | 82 |
| Developmental | Handicap swim programme | 45 | 76 |
| | Speech/language therapy | 40 | 85 |
| | Special-education class | 60 | 83 |
| Social | Integrated (regular) youth-group participation | 52 | 85 |
| Parental | PWS parent-association participation | 52 | 79 |
| | Family baby-sitting support | 45 | 76 |
| | Private baby-sitting | 40 | 85 |
| (n=42) | | | |

children. It is recommended that parents need to consider a spectrum of possibilities, starting with those that are least disruptive or detailed in their administration. Parents may wish to experiment with some of these, or to seek advice in their application or modification. One problem arising in many home-programmes is that they are sometimes difficult to carry out consistently over a period of time. Professional consultation is recommended, except in the case of very simple behavioural measures.

- Practical items, such as keeping kitchen counters clear and free of food, are considered to be an important environmental

**Table 6.2** Interventions with low-frequency and high-effectiveness ratings

| *Domain* | *Intervention* | *n* | *Effectiveness (%)* |
|---|---|---|---|
| Medical | Eye surgery | 11 | 100 |
| Allied health | Chiropractic | 5 | 80 |
| Environmental | Locks on food cupboards | 8 | 100 |
| | Lock on kitchen door | 4 | 75 |
| | No food prep. privileges | 5 | 80 |
| | No food allowed in other rooms | 11 | 91 |
| Developmental | Music therapy/training | 5 | 80 |
| Parental | Stress counselling | 9 | 100 |

control by some parents. Locking entries to kitchens, food cupboards, and refrigerators is obviously more intrusive, but where they have been used they have often proved highly effective. Many environmental controls, however, are not used by parents. They may not have thought of them – thus the importance of parent brochures summarizing advice.

- In the behavioural domain, praise seems to be more effective than isolation or deprivation of privileges, though the last two are said to be effective in some cases. Where possible, positive involvement rather than restrictive and negative practice should be employed. Positive intervention is less wearing on the children, parents, and other siblings. The aim is not just to control behaviour, but to promote positive and different behaviours. Praise affects all users, possibly improving self-image and motivation. Generally, where isolation is employed, it does not involve locking children in a room, but requesting them to remain in their room. Children are permitted to leave as soon as appropriate behaviour occurs. Punitive and abusive behaviours result in greater and longer-term disruption to all members of the family.
- Although many parents experience difficulties in joining groups, participation in PWS parents associations prove for those who use them, to be effective. Unfortunately, many parents who live in rural areas may never have had an oppor-

tunity to join such groups. These parents may be able to make contacts through telephone communication or computer networks as advisory lines are set up by provincial authorities in relation to all disabilities (e.g. Disability Information Systems of Canada).

- Parents experience many frustrations regarding professional services for their PWS dependants:
  - Medical practitioners need to be more knowledgeable about non-medical ways to help people with PWS. GPs often appear to know little about the condition, which is a major concern for parents.
  - Parents often have difficulty obtaining an effective dentist. Lists of dentists able and pleased to work with disabled children are sometimes available in major cities. Such listing is encouraged and should be regularly updated.
  - It is important that all professionals – psychologists, educators, physio- and occupational therapists, nutritionists, GPs – have a general, as well as a specific, knowledge of the local and provincial resources for PWS children provided through their own and allied professions.
- Consultation with a nutritionist or dietitian regarding dietary intervention, is helpful, though parents do not regard this as highly effective. In the majority of cases, a self-help weight-control programme does not prove particularly useful. Parents find that one of the most effective ways is to simply give their children smaller but regular portions of food.
- Special-education services are seen to be quite effective, although one of the major challenges occurs around the availability of food within school systems. It is very easy for children to obtain food from other children, garbage, and elsewhere. Education authorities need to consider how they can individualize resources in these instances. Non-teaching staff, e.g. bus drivers, janitors, secretaries, and aides, need to be informed about the child and the syndrome in order to assist in the monitoring process. It is also important to create an empathetic awareness of the problem among other children. Integration may be an important development for the educational needs of children, but if this occurs, particular attention has to be given to behavioural-management strategies regarding nutrition and food habits.

- It is important that educators do not regard PWS children as simply mentally handicapped. They are not always cognitively delayed, and when they are, some of the delay may be the result of poor motivation, self-image, and other secondary problems arising from environmental and genetic influences. It is essential that teachers are made aware of this.
- Individualized involvement is important. This arises through individual programme planning, usually under the auspices of special-education departments. Although teachers and others should be aware of the particular symptoms that are associated with PWS, interventions are often person-specific, and any strategy, while making use of general principles, should be modified to a particular child's and family's demonstrated needs. Whether individualized, special, or group programmes are used, the above guidelines should be kept in mind.
- Some children, particularly at younger ages, have found it helpful to join groups and camps. Other children find themselves isolated, or the butt of other children's remarks. The sensitivity of leaders should be taken into account in selecting any group.

*Chapter 7*

# Coping in the family

For the purposes of this discussion, coping is defined as an individual's or family's capacity to adapt successfully to the stress associated with PWS in the home.

There has been considerable research into stress and coping in a family with a handicapped member. Crnic and his colleagues (1983) presented an 'adaptational model' based on stress, coping, and ecological considerations that was formulated from the field of mental handicap. The model has applicability to a broad range of disabilities, and is of particular interest with respect to PWS families. Essentially, the handicapped child is deemed to be a significant, ongoing stressor in the family, precipitating crises of various proportions. Family response to stress utilizes available individual and corporate coping resources, which are mediated, or influenced, by the various ecological contexts in which the family operates.

Chapter 6 looked at home and community interventions, which include individual and corporate responses to the ongoing stress of parenting a PWS child; this chapter explores coping in the immediate and extended family; Chapter 8 discusses coping within major ecological contexts, that is to say, the surroundings and systems in which parents operate.

## THE PWS FAMILY

The family generally plays the primary role in the life of a non-institutionalized person with PWS. The interactive, reciprocal nature of family life both affects and is affected by the presence of a PWS member. This section is concerned with the immediate family; a discussion of the extended family follows.

## Marital stress

While some families are strengthened by the battle they together fight against PWS, others seem to disintegrate under the stress. The implications of marital instability and parental stress are profound for the PWS child, and have repercussions in other contexts such as school and community. One example is the case of an 18-year-old female referred for private counselling. Presenting behaviour problems included disrespect to those in authority at school, power struggles at home with her single-parent mother, and indecent public behaviour (urinating publicly on the street while her mother was inside shopping). Under hypnosis, the client revealed the burden of guilt and emotion she was carrying that was related to the separation of her parents two years earlier. Counselling intervention focused primarily on helping her to cope with the family separation; meanwhile, the behaviours that precipitated the referral ceased.

The paternal stress results reported in Chapter 5 suggest that PWS fathers may experience some unique syndrome-specific stresses. Some fathers resent the deprivation of the prime-time and energy of their wives. The lack of privacy in the home, reduction of time together, reduced energy levels, and differences of opinion in parenting can erode marriage stability over time. Diet and eating patterns have also been issues in some homes. Fathers have been critical of meals of 'rabbit food', and the lack of 'meat and potatoes'. It is difficult to determine, however, whether such criticisms are the product of parental stress associated with the syndrome, or whether the syndrome is a scapegoat for other marital problems.

From the maternal perspective, personal social alienation is a frequent stressor. While husbands escape from the problems of the home by going out to work each day, mothers often are left to cope with the uncertainties of daily parenting. Even simple routines such as grocery shopping or riding public transport can result in embarrassing situations that create insecurities for younger, inexperienced, or otherwise insecure mothers. As a result, some mothers have reported social withdrawal.

Perceived inequities in the parenting demands caused principally by the constant supervision requirement has also been cited as a reason for marital discord. This becomes particularly troublesome when there are differences of opinion with respect to child-rearing practices. Mothers who have dedicated themselves to the care of their PWS child and feel they receive less than optimal support from their husbands may become frustrated or angered. Thwarted career expectations or social life, for example, can then feed into building resentments. Without the opportunities for family respite, when mother and father can spend some prime-time together and recapture their collective energies, marriages are constantly at risk due to such stressors.

## Sibling attention

Some parents express concern about the imbalance in family life created by the presence of someone with special needs. Throughout childhood the concern is usually for the unmet needs of other siblings. Parents always wrestle with the extraordinary time requirements for supervision and appointments for their PWS child. Their concern for the other siblings becomes apparent at the time of adult independence, when they try to ensure that inequities do not continue. Despite parental preoccupation for future PWS dependant care, parents may be adamant in protecting siblings from inheriting the burden of care for their PWS brother or sister. In adulthood, however, siblings often provide the assurance for care and family support that is needed in the absence of parents.

## Sibling interaction

Siblings express divergent views on the experience of living with a brother or sister with PWS. This is aptly illustrated in a delightful sibling booklet entitled, 'Sometimes I'm Happy, Sometimes I'm Sad' (Janalee, 1982), in which Matt's younger sister describes what it is like to live with a brother with PWS. Feelings of unfairness at not being able to eat snacks like her friends, or feelings of embarrassment when friends visit and witness a tantrum, are balanced with expressions of sympathy and understanding.

By the teenage years there may be embarrassment at bringing friends home when cupboard and refrigerator doors are locked, or there is the possibility of witnessing inappropriate behaviours. Extra responsibilities associated with baby-sitting and other childcare functions, lack of time alone with the parent(s), and restrictions to eating routines – particularly snacking – may generate anger and resentment. From a preventive viewpoint, siblings can benefit from participation in groups focusing on personal experiences. The British Columbia Association for Community Living 'sibshops', for example, while not designed for syndrome-specific situations, can nonetheless be helpful in fostering greater understanding and coping abilities among siblings.

## Child characteristics

Several studies have suggested that certain child characteristics may be directly related to the degree of parental stress. For example, Cummings *et al.* (1966) found mothers of children with mental handicaps to be under more stress than mothers of chronically ill or neurotic children; Holroyd and McArthur (1976) found that mothers of autistic children reported more problems than mothers of Down's syndrome or out-patient psychiatric clinic children; and Holroyd and Guthrie (1979) found personal family stress to differ between children with neuromuscular and psychiatric disorders. Hence, it has been hypothesized, though not unequivocally proven, that stress may be a function of the child's particular disorder.

As seen in Chapter 5, mothers of PWS children admit to more stress than mothers of non-handicapped children, but the former are on a par with mothers of Down's syndrome children. In fact, the profile of stress for the PWS and Down's syndrome mothers has been shown to be similar on a small sample (James, 1987). Child responsiveness, temperament, repetitive behaviour patterns, and the presence of additional or unusual care-giving demands have been found to be significantly related to the amount of stress reported by parents of handicapped infants; the number of additional care-giving demands made upon the parent was the variable most highly related to stress (Beckman, 1983). The authors noted that the strong pattern of intercorrelations found among responsiveness, temperament, and care-giving demands suggests that the three may draw from a single 'difficulty to care dimension'. The testimony of PWS parents is strongly supportive of Beckman's results.

## Family adaptation

While much research related to mental handicap has focused on differences between the families of handicapped and non-handicapped children, there is a need to look at within-group differences when examining coping mechanisms (Crnic *et al.*, 1983). Several trends in PWS family adaptations were observed during the course of the study by James (1987). Adaptation for the purpose of this discussion refers to changes that affect the family as a unit, not simply individual members.

## Eating patterns

> He was helping himself to things on the side and gaining weight and gaining more weight until finally we had to put him in the hospital.

The primary adaptation required to maintain the well-being of any person with PWS relates to eating patterns. Hermann (1981) found a moderate-to-severe impact on family eating habits in 70% of the PWS families studied. Some 65% of all PWS families in the study by James (1987) had tried calorie counting as an intervention; approximately 40% had tried a food-exchange system and/or a special diet. Such interventions impinge on the eating habits of all family members. Specific examples of adaptations to eating patterns included:

- ensuring regular meal times;
- allowing food to be eaten only in the dining area;
- providing only low-calorie snack items;
- colour-coding food containers (e.g. green=skimmed milk, red=whole milk) for young children;
- serving one portion only;
- restricting availability of desserts;
- limiting dining out;
- avoiding junk foods;
- using low-calorie substitutes;

- altering cooking habits;
- enforcing table etiquette and rituals.

As a consequence of such adaptations, parents and siblings often resorted to clandestine patterns of eating. Parents confessed to consuming junk food in the privacy of their locked bedroom, and sneaking extra portions of food to other siblings after bedtime hours. They repeatedly commented on the acute hearing of the PWS child, for example responding to the sound of cellophane wrappings from distant rooms.

The differential treatment of siblings regarding access to food, privileges in the kitchen, and purchasing habits was on occasion a source of family tension. In a few instances the inflexible meat-and-potatoes expectation of the father created inordinate food presentation problems for the mother. Hence, adaptations to eating patterns, so essential for dietary control of the PWS child, may give rise to socially less-desirable actions such as hiding food and sneaking, and reactions such as obstinacy, anger, and hostility from other family members.

## Environmental controls

> I used to have to put a lock on the fridge when he first started this eating stuff. He was two and one-half.

A second trend towards environmental controls within the home to prevent access to food was evident, and consistent with parent literature (Heinemann and Tomaseski-Heinemann, 1983; Pipes, 1981; Sechrist, 1986). Physical controls involved securing existing food-storage areas (locks on kitchen entry doors, cupboards, refrigerators, and freezers); modifying existing premises to ensure the security of food storage (converting an extra bedroom to a lockable pantry; installing a decorative wrought-iron gate to secure the archway entrance to a modern kitchen); and enforcing strict kitchen routines (counters always cleared; restricted access to the kitchen). The degree of environmental control varied with each family situation, but generally occurred across all ages.

Controls were most critical in independent living situations. In one instance, no food was kept in the flat, and all meals were brought in from a nearby group home; in another situation, a live-in attendant (dietary aide) was responsible for all food management and security.

It was noted by several parents that environmental controls are not static: the child's skill at obtaining food increases with age, necessitating more sophisticated controls. With a younger child, for example, food may simply be placed out of reach, but eventually it must be out of sight and even under lock. Locks, however, have been attacked with tools in order to gain access to secured food. Several parents reported a need to rotate food between locked storage cupboards, carry keys on their person so they could not be found, and restrict access to the kitchen area even when cupboards were locked.

### Alternative residential options

> My first concern is about her living at home. How long am I going to be able to take care of her?

Parents of teenagers and young adults consistently sought information on the alternative residential options available for PWS adults. Their concerns were usually precipitated by parental burn-out from a prolonged burden of care; recognition of their own advancing age and the need to make provision for their PWS dependant; or a concern for normalization of the young adult, including full integration into the community.

The question of alternative residence is emotionally laden for many parents (Greenswag, 1984a), particularly parents of teenagers. Parents of PWS adults in their 20s and 30s often acknowledged the inevitability of a move; parents of teenagers were often torn between the responsibility to parent and the desire for an out-of-home placement for their special child. Both groups expressed frustration, and in some cases anger, over the lack of residential options available to their PWS dependants.

The trend toward alternative-living situations has resulted from the normalization movement (Wolfensberger, 1972). Parents and PWS dependants alike have had their expectations raised with the movement toward de-institutionalization and community integration for handicapped persons. The application of social and fiscal policy, however, varies across and within provinces. While there are usually few options in any one locale, the overall perspective includes a number of models identified in the study by James (1987), including living in the family home; a boarding home; a group home for mentally handicapped persons; a behavioural or therapeutic group home; a PWS group home; a mental health or extended-care institution; an independent-living setting with attendant support; or an independent-living setting with itinerant support.

These options have been expanded to ten models, including attached suite, denominational facilities, and co-habitation, and are illustrated with case examples by James and Willott (1989). Such options are attractive to parents, who often suffer personally under a prolonged burden of care. Where children had made a move away from the family home, parents frequently reported improved parent–child relationships, better spousal relations, maturation of the child, and weight loss for the child.

## Separation or divorce

> She required a lot of time and effort, and then there was the second child, and I think the dad just felt kind of out of the picture. He never wanted to be involved in any of the physio or . . . any of the speech development. And he just chose to leave the situation.

In some families, an unfortunate response to the presence of inordinate stress caused by the presence of a PWS child is marital breakdown. While only a few mothers acknowledged that their PWS child contributed to their divorce or separation, the present study raises questions regarding the frequency of separation or divorce as a parental option in a stressful family situation. The high stress levels of fathers in intact marriages, and the below-average number of intact marriages, suggests that alterations to the marital partnership may indeed be a coping strategy. Other PWS writers have indicated considerable disruption of family living (Hermann, 1981), and the possibility of parental conflicts as a result of different values in child-rearing practices (Leconte, 1981). Hermann reported two cases of separation and divorce between PWS parents which at least in part related to the presence of a PWS child. Although causal relationship is difficult to establish, separation and divorce are adaptations to family structure that have implications for parental coping and child well-being. The suggestion by Crnic *et al*. (1983) that marital satisfaction may decrease over time in families with retarded children may be of particular relevance to PWS.

## Social alienation

> There has been one [social situation] that really bothers me and I am avoiding it . . .

Mothers of young children described the embarrassment of taking their child to a neighbourhood birthday party, a festive family gathering, or simply grocery shopping in a supermarket. Several admitted to avoiding social situations that would result in embarrassment to the child or themselves. Parents of adolescents expressed frustrations at the restrictions on their social life when they could not leave their child alone or with a babysitter; those with adult PWS dependants similarly admitted that the supervision requirements of their dependant consumed a major part of their energy.

These indicators of social alienation are supported by the SCL-90-R results for women. The subscales of significance suggest self-perception that could lead to social alienation. For example, 'interpersonal-sensitivity' focuses on feelings of inadequacy, inferiority, and discomfort during interpersonal interactions; 'depression' involves withdrawal, lack of motivation, and loss of energy; and 'psychoticism' ranges from mild interpersonal alienation to psychosis. That mothers may be particularly prone to social alienation is consistent with earlier discussion suggesting that they often carry the weight of caregiving responsibilities alone. By contrast, fathers usually have the benefit of meaningful personal and social contacts through employment.

The foregoing paragraphs describe some family adaptations to the presence of a PWS dependant. It must be emphasized again, however, that families respond differently to such a dependant. Furthermore, the number and severity of problems associated with raising a PWS child differs across families.

Adaptations may be conscious or unconscious, and often occur gradually over time.

## PERSONAL COPING STRATEGIES

Within family units, various strategies are employed by individuals to maintain personal and corporate equilibrium. Coping strategies reflect the nature of the coping resources available (Friedrich *et al.*, 1985), and may be of long or short duration. The strategies which follow reflect common, more personal approaches to the amelioration of parental stress.

### Behaviour management techniques

> He resents being left home with a baby-sitter. He will throw all his clothes down the laundry-chute, or empty all of the toothpaste out.

Behavioural-management strategies were identified by parents as the primary parental need. The behavioural domain was also seen to have the greatest utility in terms of intervention. Scores within this domain, however, showed the greatest discrepancy of views.

Praise was the most effective approach of all interventions surveyed; deprivation of food, isolation, and physical punishment were considered to be three of the four most ineffective interventions. Clearly, more attempts were made to use behavioural interventions than those of any other domain. Just as clear, however, is the range of results obtained. When confronted with inappropriate child behaviours, most parents admit to attempting disciplinary practices. Punitive measures have been viewed as both effective (deprivation of privileges, isolation) and ineffective (deprivation of food, physical punishment and isolation). By contrast, the affirmative practice of praise was consistently perceived as effective. Few parents, if any, had any training in parenting. Given the centrality of behaviour problems in working with PWS, and the expressed need of parents for more behavioural skills, there is a definite need to provide information on behaviour-management principles for PWS parents.

### Respite care

> Since we've got this respite care thing, it's got a lot better. How she was getting along with us was really a concern, like divorce time almost.

Respite care, in the form of agency-supplied parent-relief time, was considered to be very effective by the parents who had used it. While most older parents did not have respite services available in earlier years, younger parents were almost universally taking advantage of respite when available. In a few cases, parents of PWS adult dependants were unaware of their eligibility for present services; in other cases there was no service available. In one instance, the parents of a ten-year-old child recounted the lack of respite service as their child had been considered learning disabled and not mentally handicapped, and hence had not met local eligibility criteria.

There are great variations in the amount of respite care available, the cost to parents, and eligibility requirements within and across provinces. Generally, respite care is delivered as home-based care, group day-care, an activity programme, or as an adjunct relief service at community residences for handicapped persons.

Respite was viewed as a coping strategy for parents in most cases, although there was recognition of its benefits for the child as well, providing a break from the tensions of the home, facilitating peer contacts and socialization activities, and encouraging steps towards independence. For some parents, availability of trained staff to provide care eased the guilt associated with leaving their child; for all, the opportunity for respite seemed to relieve family stress and improve relationships.

### Child therapy

> She attends the awkward children's movement clinic.

Child therapy was most often used to remediate developmental disabilities (infant stimulation, handicap swim programme, speech and language training); change aberrant behaviours (counselling, psychotherapy); or, to a much lesser degree, optimize potential (art therapy, music therapy, sports).

Most parents relied on professional referral before considering a course in therapy. Value conflicts between parents, as pointed out by Leconte (1981), sometimes result in a rejection of treatment opportunity for a child; parental burn-out has the same effect on occasion. Additionally, the potential benefits of therapy were often thwarted by a lack of knowledge about therapies available; parental preconceptions about potential value of the therapy; social stigma associated with being under treatment; and the financial consideration of who will pay. Parents frequently blame the syndrome for everything, thus avoiding dealing with behavioural, social, and personal care issues that could be addressed in therapy with present knowledge.

## Parent therapy

> If I'm going to die, I might as well commit suicide and take him with me. You know, what is the future?

Most parents seem to resist involvement in therapy, as illustrated by the low numbers responding to the items related to stress counselling, marital counselling, or family therapy. The low-effectiveness rating for these latter two interventions probably reflects the crisis nature of the problem when therapy was attempted. Primary factors seeming to mitigate against earlier preventive therapy include the social stigma of treatment, the degree of marital discord, and the failure to acknowledge the severity of stress. Parent-directed therapies often require the support and involvement of the spouse, and in some cases other family members. Hence, those parents most in need are often the least likely to become involved. The need is evident for low-cost parent support before the situation becomes a crisis.

## Parent-support groups

> There was a small circle of three and we did meet occasionally, either in twos or threes and exchanged information a

> bit. It made us feel that we weren't alone, although we might be a scarce commodity.

While two-thirds of the PWS parents had tried affiliating with a PWS parent organization, distance in many cases mitigated against full participation. At the time of writing, PWS parent group meetings are held in only four urban centres in western Canada to the writers' knowledge (Vancouver, Calgary, Edmonton, Winnipeg). Some parents maintained membership in the American Prader–Willi Syndrome Association, while others affiliated with the closest Canadian group. In some cases parents held memberships in two or more groups. Those from more rural areas chiefly benefit from the communication provided through newsletters; urban residents can take full advantage of association involvement, including peer support, group advocacy, professional referrals, and meaningful service opportunities. The American Prader–Willi Syndrome Association, in functioning as a clearinghouse, put several Canadians in touch with others; this role is now being taken over by the newly established Canadian groups. While most parents seem to want to affiliate, to share in the common bond, and to receive the communication benefits, few opt for active involvement.

## Religion

> Why me? What have I done to deserve this? I think I came to terms with it in a way that my spiritual life gave me strength to cope with it. I came to terms with it and just gave it over to the Lord and just took one day at a time . . . You know, the biggest comfort that I had was where it says in scripture that you should not worry about tomorrow, look at the birds in the air and the flowers in the field. And that was the biggest thing that got me through . . . I kind of surrendered it to the Lord and you live in that strength.

Persons expressing a faith display a strength that helps them to cope with stress, as exemplified in the above excerpt. The parent quoted mentioned the gratification received from the acceptance of his son in the life of the church: attending Sunday school, receiving baptism, singing solo before the congregation.

Churches have provided an outlet for musical interest, involvement in youth activities, and the development of a meaningful spiritual dimension for some individuals with PWS. For parents, the community of support and counselling services were pragmatic coping resources similar to those mentioned by Leconte (1981). The relatively low number of PWS families actively practising a religion may be a factor in the social alienation discussed earlier.

## Counselling

Counselling may be viewed as a personal coping strategy, or an intervention in family adaptation. It is treated here as a separate topic because of its importance. As a verb, 'to counsel' means to give advice; in its archaic form it implied wisdom or judgment.

There is confusion in the 'marketplace' with respect to counselling. On the one hand, counsel may be delivered by a neighbour, who may be a good listener with available time; on the other hand, there are a variety of individuals who present themselves as 'professional' counsellors, and who charge a substantial sum for their services. Somewhere in between are professionals from almost every other discipline who may see the giving of advice, or counsel, as part of their professional responsibility to their client.

As there is little regulation of counselling practices in most jurisdictions, parents must be alert when shopping for services. If considering a professional counsellor, it is reasonable to question the counsellor's professional affiliations, that is to say, the professional counselling organizations in which memberships are held. Usually these can be found by examining the certificates hanging on the wall. All professional bodies are self-regulated by a code of ethical conduct to which members must adhere. This provides a measure of consumer recourse in the event of professional impropriety.

It is also reasonable to enquire about the counselling methodologies. Some counsellors operate within a narrow philosophical framework, while others are very eclectic, selecting their interventions from a broader range of sources. In larger centres it may be possible to check fee schedules through officers of the professional organization; in smaller centres a telephone call to most government social services agencies can usually produce direct information or a more appropriate referral. Hornby (in press) points out that counsellors providing services to families with members with disabilities should have a knowledge of the adaptation process and dynamics of families of people with disabilities; attitudes consistent with the development of a positive partnership; and good interpersonal skills, including listening, understanding, and problem-solving.

In the case of low-incidence conditions it is desirable that a counsellor should have previous experience in working with the specific disability. The reality, however, is that there are not many professional counsellors with experience in working with PWS. Word-of-mouth advertising is very important, and parents most often rely on the recommendation of other parents when seeking this professional assistance.

As mentioned above, many professionals from other disciplines may also offer counsel about PWS. Such counsel, however, should be restricted to their own areas of expertise. When professionals begin to make recommendations outside the scope of their own discipline, parents should be cautious and question the grounds for such recommendations. As cited elsewhere, there have been criticisms of individuals giving advice which is inappropriate. On the other hand, it may be that a professional with an interest in PWS has acquired a great deal of transdisciplinary knowledge through study and direct experience, which can be imparted to the parents without the need to see and pay for another professional.

The use of lay counsellors has increased in the last few decades. In many communities, non-profit societies, religious organizations, and self-help groups provide counselling to those unable to afford professional services. Often the delivery of support may be on a group-counselling basis, rather than individualized, in such areas as advocacy or parenting skills. These groups may facilitate networking with other parents in need, and also be able to respond quickly to the support needs of parents in times of crisis. While there is much to recommend in group-counselling approaches, it would be unusual for there to be a PWS-specific focus unless the group was a PWS parent-support group.

## THE EXTENDED FAMILY

The extended family includes individuals within the family who do not reside in the family home, other than parents and siblings. Grandparents, aunts, uncles, and cousins are in this group. Not so many years ago the family would have included all relatives; today a differentiation is made, based on the degree of involvement in the life of the subject concerned. The primary factor distinguishing nuclear or extended-family membership is usually location of residence. Hence a grandparent living in the family home would be considered a member of the nuclear family, yet the same individual living across town, in another city, or out of the province would be considered an extended-family member. Obviously, extended-family members may have a vested interest in the welfare of the PWS child, although the level of involvement will vary considerably.

### Personal struggles

Grandparents, aunts, uncles, and cousins are usually overlooked when information is initially given about PWS. Hence, they get their information second-hand from the parents or third- or fourth-hand from each other. In such instances the objectivity of the clinician is replaced with the subjectivity of the parent or other family member.

It must be recognized that the emotions surrounding the diagnosis, for nuclear or extended-family members, can mirror those of the parents: shock, disbelief, disappointment, unwillingness to accept, or a desire to fight are not uncommon. Grandparents especially may face great struggles. As with the first child, particular importance is often attributed to the first grandchild. The decision of parents not to conceive again, whether made out of haste and reaction, or duly considered after counselling, may be difficult for the grandparents to accept, depending on the number of grandchildren and the potential to multiply the family name. It is unfortunate, too, that inappropriate blame may be directed at one of the parents. This may result from a lack of biomedical information, as a reaction to a perceived insult to the family name, or even spitefully if preceded by other family-relationship problems. The extended-family member also must cope with the personal meaning of the diagnosis and the reaction of the parents. In home visits with over 50 PWS families, only one extended-family member, a maternal grandmother, sat in on the interviews. Some parents related that the grandparents were unable to cope with their child due to failing health, reduced energy levels, and the supervision requirements.

### Source of support

Relatives can be a great source of support, particularly for child-care and baby-sitting, significant relationships for the child, and emotional support to the parents. Examples can be cited of grandparents providing accommodation when a marriage dissolved, aunts and uncles supplying parent respite and summer holiday opportunities for children, and cousins providing social companionship. Unfortunately, today the supportive role of the extended family is frequently compounded by the mobility and distance factor. Parents often find themselves raising their children without the support of extended-family members.

On the other hand, the presence of extended-family members is not always positive. Relatives without an appreciation of PWS are cited as major problems. Lack of respect for dietary and behavioural controls inevitably adds to family stress. One single parent of a nine-year-old girl lamented the situation with grandparents, saying, 'We only have one set of grandparents to deal with', but the frustration was evident as she carried on to say that despite giving them the literature on PWS, she must each time reiterate 'exactly what she can have to eat' because the grandmother likes 'to feed her things'. Since dietary control is such an important part of a mother's role, it is a frequent point of contention.

### Estrangement

Withdrawal from contact or estrangement is not unknown. In one situation, strong cultural family traditions centring around food contributed to family relationship problems, with mother and child initially absenting themselves from extended-family functions, and ultimately from the marriage. In another case, married siblings chose not to maintain much contact with their PWS sister, who had moved into semi-independent living. In several situations grandparents have chosen not to visit their children and grandchild due to the personal stress experienced. Shame, embarrassment, confusion as to how to personally handle interactions, and disagreement with parenting approaches have been reasons attributed to relatives who have reduced the number or length of contacts.

## SUMMARY

Chapter 7 has examined coping within the family. Individual and corporate attempts at stress management in response to the presence of a PWS family member were considered.

- Adaptations around family eating patterns are generally required. Arranging regular mealtimes, allowing food to be eaten only in the dining area, providing low-calorie snacks, colour-coding food containers, serving only one portion of food, restricting desserts, limited dining out, and avoiding the presence of junk foods can all be helpful. But such restrictions cause stress for families, and counselling and advice is required; it is important to find the most appropriate measures for particular family situations.
- It is important that parents, and particularly mothers, have opportunities to get out of the home and experience outings that are stress-free, as well as having time to attend to their personal nutritional and social needs. The same applies to siblings.
- There is often additional stress in relation to marriage. Marriage or family counselling, with attention to siblings living at home, is important. Parents should not regard counselling as a need just because they are worried or are mentally stressed, but should seek guidance and support to assure maximum and healthy running of the family. One of the consequences of a community-orientated, rather than a facility-based rehabilitation service is that governments need to ensure that some of the funds saved from down-sizing

institutions are used to support families at risk, and to provide counselling before breakdown occurs.

- Parents should be made aware of the variety of home or residential options that are possible. No one type of living environment is suitable for all PWS children. Obviously, the specific needs of both parents and children must be borne in mind. Residential and institutional placements are not necessarily better today than in the past, nor are they necessarily the most supportive or helpful to parents. In Canada, a range of residential options has been employed to meet the unique needs of the individual, family, and community circumstances. A major issue relates to the ability of the family and the person with PWS to control eating behaviours. The more these are controlled, the more likely that a variety of home-living models can be made available.
- The need for respite is critical. Family stress levels suggest that access to funded services is an almost universal need. Even short-term child-sitting can be a major problem, restricting parent involvement outside of the home. Practical advice on the selection and guidance of child-sitters is necessary.
- It is important that parent manuals, which provide straightforward advice in non-technical language, including lists of potential resources, be made available. There is a dearth of behavioural information which is PWS-specific.
- Relatives can be a great source of support, although they are not always available in our mobile society. Their education and understanding is important for family harmony, as well as for their role in supporting the PWS child.
- Some parents have found personal support through their church, parent-support groups, or structured therapy. Parents are encouraged to pursue support as a preventive measure rather than leaving it to a crisis stage.

*Chapter 8*

# Coping in the community

While the previous chapter dealt with coping in the context of the nuclear and extended family, this chapter looks at coping within the community. The examples included illustrate in practical terms the importance of the ecological perspective in understanding how parents of PWS children cope with stress. The authors' experience suggests that at present the various ecological contexts often augment, rather than moderate, the stress levels of PWS families. This is to be expected, given the lack of professional and public awareness of the syndrome.

## THE NEIGHBOURHOOD

Parental supervision usually restricts PWS children, to their immediate neighbourhood. The supervision requirements continue to impose restrictions through the teenage and adult years, with few individuals ever achieving the degree of community independence experienced by their non-handicapped peers.

The neighbourhood is not truly a microcosm of the larger community; more often it is a homogeneous grouping based on socio-economic or cultural factors. As such it often provides shelter from the world. On the other hand, for those previously sheltered within the home it represents a world of opportunity to explore. Most children and youth with PWS possess a curiosity about their neighbourhood which will lead naturally to exploration. Restrictions imposed by those with concerns for food access are often in conflict with natural developmental experiences, which contribute to child frustration.

## Rural vs urban differences

One mother of a 29-year-old male in a rural village revealed a degree of confidence when she said, 'this is a small community, everyone knows him'. With that knowledge, her son was free to move about the community in a way that would have been very difficult in an urban centre. In another illustration, a young woman with PWS was permitted to drive her parent's car within the small town, but was not permitted to venture beyond. The natural geographic features helped to define the boundaries, restricting her whereabouts to a comfortable radius. One can speculate about the potential problems that could arise with a young person with PWS having a driver's licence in a metropolitan area.

Even public transit services create a problem in larger centres, facilitating independence but often courting disaster. In a large city, a teenager was transported to school daily by taxi because of her inability to control food access when she rode the public bus system. Despite being driven to the schoolyard, however, she still had time to visit a nearby corner shop after being dropped off. In the same city, on the other hand, a PWS woman of 25 years of age was able to ride the commuter train and transfer and take a bus, for a total of 45 minutes transportation one-way, in order to attend a vocational training programme. She had done this twice daily for several years without appreciable influence on her weight. Thus while the rural or urban context presents certain pragmatic problems, the effect on the individual is mediated by personal characteristics, which differ from person to person.

## Community awareness

Some parents find it necessary to advise neighbours, local food outlets, and convenience shops of the food addiction of their child. One parent of a 16-year-old lamented the energy required to maintain neighbourly relations after his son, on separate occasions, had stolen a dish full of sweets, food from the freezer, and the neighbour's car. This same boy's affinity for keys resulted in the theft of the neighbour's key-ring, which was subsequently dropped through a manhole cover as he attempted to avoid being caught.

On the positive side, neighbours can provide a support network to monitor the child's whereabouts, maintain the diet, and provide meaningful social experiences and relationships. To the degree that the neighbourhood is a miniature of the community at large it offers many of the same temptations. Parents seem most concerned with the access to food and the child's vulnerability to the leading of others.

The neighbourhood is particularly important for those adults with PWS who move into a community setting. A recurrent lament from parents of PWS persons who are living in apartment blocks, for example, is the lack of supportive contacts with neighbours. Most people dwelling in apartments, however, lead independent lifestyles that do not involve much contact with neighbours in general. Loneliness is one of the major issues facing those persons with handicaps who try to integrate into the mainstream of our communities. Parents naturally share the agony of that loneliness.

## Parental relief

It is natural for parents to look to others in the neighbourhood for baby-sitting support, particularly where members of the extended family are not close to hand. While baby-sitters are often found through word-of-mouth, parents of special-needs children are increasingly looking to community social services agencies or baby-sitting associations for recommendations of qualified sitters.

It is not unusual for PWS children to react differently to relationships with baby-sitters and other surrogate care-givers. One mother of a 'loveable, affectionate, very pretty little girl' of eight years described her daughter's reaction to the presence of a baby-sitter:

> I have never experienced a violent tantrum with her, but I've seen the marks she will leave. But these terrible episodes are only with a baby-sitter. Anyone who she is left in the care of has been a friend or neighbour who Ann has a great usual relationship with. Her current baby-sitter and her get along

> fine most of the time. But when a temper-tantrum comes, Ann will kick, or scratch or bite or throw things and scream obscenities. This is not just with this sitter but with anyone she is left with. (*PWS Newsletter – Canada*, March, 1989.)

The fear of such reactions often deters parents from going out, and baby-sitters from return engagements.

In a recent Canadian article, the mother of a teenager described how she desperately needed assistance. Her own mother had been suffering ill health, and could no longer provide parental relief. Additionally, the daughter had required surgery. In response, the local association set up a respite situation for six weeks to cover the period of convalescence. The adolescent residence, however, closed its doors a few months later, sending the parents into a panic. After 16 years without a holiday with her husband, plans had been made for a spring vacation. A relief family was found for the period of the holiday, but because of the child's challenging behaviours they could not continue to offer relief afterwards. Next, a Special Needs At-Home Service Agreement (additional social services funds for a respite worker) brought 12-hours-per-week respite in the form of community experiences for the child and free time for the parent. When the worker left to return to university, there was another five-month wait to find a suitable replacement. After hearing of the success of another family in finding relief through a church, the parents discussed the matter of support with their pastor and advertised in the parish bulletin. The end result was that several families volunteered to assist in providing relief. In the words of the parents, 'Having four families offering weekend support means Rachelle had a new experience each month. We had our relief and the families were activated only once every four months for weekend visits, sometimes more often if only an evening was involved' (King, 1988).

Such relief is seldom one-sided. The child as well as the parents invariably benefit. In Rachelle's case, 'she has grown as an individual because of the experiences she has had with these people. She enjoys having interesting tales to share with the family and others. She gets very excited anticipating her next weekend away from home'. The parents testify that this has 'not been a perfect answer,' but it is an alternative that has been a 'life-saver'. Church communities can be a valuable resource for those who are able to 'swallow their pride and ask'.

The provision of parent relief through formal respite services is important for helping to maintain the integrity of the special-needs family unit. Informal parent relief through traditional baby-sitting sources may be difficult to obtain and unsatisfactory in performance. Even swapping children with other PWS parents, or parents of other special-needs children, may be difficult, particularly in smaller rural communities. Unfortunately there may be inequities in eligibility criteria and availability of funding across jurisdictions for short-term respite. Parents should contact the local government social services department for assistance.

## Abuse

According to Greenswag (1988) there are no data to suggest that children with PWS are sexually abused more than comparable handicapped children. Recent research conducted at the University of Alberta, however, indicates that people with disabilities in general are more likely to be subjected to sexual abuse and assault than their non-handicapped peers. The risk factor appears to be at least 150% greater than for individuals of the same sex and similar age without disabilities (Sobsey, 1988).

The fear of sexual abuse has been expressed by many parents. Whether individuals with PWS are more vulnerable than other developmentally disabled groups has not been determined empirically. Parent fears are often based on impaired cognitive functioning (lack of understanding of sexual knowledge; inability to reason through social situations); lack of sexual attractiveness to normal peers (more likely to respond to anyone offering attention); desire for positive physical attention (because previously experienced physical attention has been clinical and negative); gullibility to the leading of others (easily influenced to try new things in the absence of supervision); and the use of food as a motivator (more easily coerced or bribed).

Research indicates that developmentally disabled persons are at higher risk of abuse because of generally impaired communication skills; the inability to physically defend themselves; and environmental factors, such as family stress, parental isolation, demoralization, and chronic anxiety. Disabled children are also more likely to live outside the family home. Children in institutions; group homes; single-, remarried- and foster-parent homes have been found to be at greater risk for abuse. Similarly, specialized medical, social, and educational services also increase the risk (Sobsey, 1988).

The teaching of compliance in the school system has been cited by Sobsey as an area of concern. Compliance may be of particular concern with PWS children, as the provision of much structure and supervision is required in the home as well. Children are taught to comply with the requests of teachers, parents, and responsible adults, associating resistance with negative consequences. Unfortunately, disabled children may generalize their compliance 'lessons' to inappropriate situations, thus becoming more vulnerable to possible abuse.

Parents should be aware that symptoms of sexual abuse may erroneously be attributed to the child's disability, and therefore go unidentified. Withdrawal, sleep disturbances, and resistance to physical examination are common symptoms. In an unreported case of sexual abuse of a 19-year-old female with PWS, the symptoms were masked by the victim: having moved out of her mother's home to live in the home of her boyfriend and his parents, the girl was persuaded to keep an appointment made by her mother, who was determined to have her examined by a doctor. The daughter went to the doctor's office, but cancelled the appointment. The daughter later described sexually abusive activities by her boyfriend, and was found to have contracted chlamydia, a sexually transmitted disease, from him.

On a more positive note, females with PWS have reported potentially dangerous situations in which they were able to exercise judgment and control to protect themselves. In one case, a 23-year-old woman living alone in an apartment block was approached by an older male offering her food if she would go to his flat. She rebuffed his approach, and reported the incident to her family.

Griffiths *et al.* (1989) argue that the learning of appropriate socio-sexual expression should be a standard component of training for all persons with handicaps. Sexual expression for persons with handicaps in general, however, is still largely taboo. This taboo is often perpetuated by PWS families. Uncertainties surrounding the implications of 'incomplete sexual development' and procreative capacity no doubt enhance the difficult parental position. Unfortunately, a lack of basic understanding of sexuality and personal safety skills may result, leaving the PWS child more vulnerable than protected.

## THE MEDICAL SYSTEM

All PWS families interact extensively with the medical system. The intensity of normal involvement usually peaks at diagnosis, and thereafter maintains a moderate level of ongoing contact, unless there are complications related to dual diagnosis or crises warranting medical intervention.

### The role of medical doctors

While services from GPs are not rated highly by a substantial number of parents, the services of specialists such as paediatricians and endocrinologists are positively acknowledged. In fairness to GPs, it must be understood that most were not acquainted with PWS in their training, and may never have had previous experience with it in their years of practice. Even today it is the medical specialists who usually provide the diagnosis or diagnostic confirmation; they are the ones most likely to be called on to answer parents' questions. While the number of professional articles related to PWS has increased in medical journals during the last two decades, there is still a need to educate medical practitioners to both the medical and non-medical aspects of the syndrome.

It must be reiterated that the interaction of parent and medical practitioner often occurs in an emotionally charged environment. Drotar (1981) describes the relationship of physician and family as an ambivalent partnership in which treatment and cure do not equate. He also suggests that physicians generally are ill-prepared for, and inexperienced with, home-based management of the chronically ill, and that communication between the physician and the family may be less than optimal. A similar view is expressed by Doernberg (1982), who explains that because paediatricians are untrained in the treatment and management of psycho-social and behavioural problems, they may hesitate to broach these subjects with families. This hesitancy is viewed by some parents as a lack of interest in providing ongoing support. GPs are the most often criticized in this regard. On the other hand, there are medical personnel who readily give advice in these areas when it would be more appropriate to refer to personnel in another discipline.

Until medical doctors have more prognostic information available to them and know the resources in the community, including treatment and training strategies, they will have difficulty answering the vital questions of parents. They must also recognize and refer to the other disciplines working with PWS in order to contribute in comprehensive syndrome management.

## Mediators of stress

The professional manner and competence of medical doctors is important in mediating child and parental stress. It is possible, however, that some medical personnel unwittingly contribute to the stress of some family situations. While the vignettes presented in Chapter 2 represent parental admission of distress, it is likely that the doctors involved were unaware of the stress they were causing. One mother, recalling her frustration with a GP, said, 'there wasn't an ounce of support. He didn't give anything.' Another who received the diagnosis over the phone claimed she was, 'really depressed about it, it was really negative.'

The manner of diagnosis, attitude of the doctor, lack of information given, impersonal approach, and lack of follow-up support have all been criticized. Some parents have indicated that some doctors simply do not have a good bedside manner or counselling skills, despite being extremely competent in their field. The end result for some parents, unfortunately, is a reluctance to pursue issues clinically until absolutely essential. Given that children with PWS do not respond to pain and infection in the same way as their non-PWS peers, any delay in obtaining medical service might be dangerous.

The frustrations expressed by parents with respect to the

medical system need to be addressed. There is a need for greater understanding on the part of parents and physicians. Medical doctors must become more knowledgeable with respect to PWS, particularly its psycho-social implications; correspondingly, parents must be educated to the scope and limitations of medical supports available to them.

As mentioned earlier, often there is a discrepancy between parental expectations and what the medical system can reasonably deliver. However, with improvements in basic knowledge related to PWS and in communication, much parent stress might be averted. Somewhat ironically, the real experts with PWS are the parents, yet they resort to medical professionals for answers to often unanswerable questions. As evidenced in the study by James (1987) and reported in the earlier chapters, parents are becoming involved in the research process. Importantly, medical professionals need to hear of their experiences. As one father stated, 'It wasn't as hopeless as what the doctors had said it was going to be. And now it is our concern trying to get the medical profession to learn what we have learned.'

## The specialists

The mystique about the medical profession is often confusing to parents, particularly those who are inexperienced in working with the health-care system. Medical and allied health specialists who might be involved with PWS can be found in Appendix C. Parents should not be intimidated by the white coats, sterile settings, and medical jargon. Instead they should insist upon a lay interpretation and 'consumer' satisfaction. It also is important that parents understand the limits of the medical speciality, which is particularly important when discussing a prognosis. The neonatologist may be able to talk about the implications of the syndrome beyond the neonate stage, and the paediatrician may be able to provide information relevant to young adulthood, but neither is necessarily qualified to give prognostic information relative to longevity and adult quality-of-life issues that may be of concern to parents.

Parents need to have their questions answered in terms they can understand. They have a right to information about their child's disability, and what a treatment programme will mean for the child and the family. The right to participate in decision-making about a child implies access to the necessary information; it also assumes the right to seek a second opinion if a parent is dissatisfied with a diagnosis or recommended treatment. Table 8.1 suggests some topics parents might want to explore with the medical specialist.

**Table 8.1** Topics to explore with a medical specialist

| |
|---|
| Feeding |
| Dietary management |
| Weight control |
| Physical abnormalities |
| Mental development |
| Sexual development |
| Oral/dental development |
| Vision/hearing/speech |
| Skin condition/skin-picking |
| Scoliosis/skeletal problems |
| Thermo-regulation issues |
| Infections |
| Recommended treatments/therapies |
| Eligibility for services |
| Specialist referrals |
| Chromosome testing |
| Ongoing monitoring |
| Genetic counselling |
| PWS research programmes |
| Support-group contacts |

### A partnership model

Parents and medical practitioners have the same primary concern: the welfare of the PWS child or adult. It is logical, therefore, that there should be a partnership approach to the task of PWS management. Parents need to have reaffirmed that they too are 'professional' in the sense that they have expertise about PWS. They have studied, attended conferences, participated in associations, and 'served time' equivalent to internships. Informed parents can do much to enhance the partnership with medical professionals. The mutual quest for information and the sharing of literature is easier when there is a concept of partnership.

The onus is on the parents to propose the model. They must state their desire for involvement and define their focus or contribution. They must be willing to explore intervention strategies and do the record-keeping required to assist in monitoring interventions. They also need to be available to attend meetings or to consult.

What is being encouraged under a partnership model implies a good degree of parental assertiveness, which should not be confused with aggressiveness. A 'parent professional' must also respect the medical professional and behave in an ethical manner. It is important that both recognize the limits of their expertise, and acknowledge the contribution of the partner.

## THE EDUCATION SYSTEM

The education system plays an extremely important role during the years of child and adolescent development. It is a universal requirement for children to be educated, and the system has the child for a larger block of time than any other service provider. While parents may have had limited experience with the medical system, and possibly none with the social services system, all parents have had personal experiences with the education system. Despite changes in the system since their own schooldays, and their experience of regular, and not special education, parents nevertheless have memories and opinions about the education system that may colour their expectations and relationships.

Most public education systems in Canada operate on a 'zero-reject' concept, that is, all students presenting themselves for instruction will be accepted. Placement may be in special schools, special classes, regular classes, or combinations of these. This is not the case, however, with private systems. An interesting case in point is that of a 13-year-old PWS female who was finishing primary school in the public system and had been recommended for a special-class placement in junior secondary school. The parent, however, chose to try to enrol her in a private school for students with learning disabilities.

The parent used an advocate who was able to present a profile with distinctive strengths and weaknesses based on standardized test results. The child was accepted because she fitted the mandate of the private school, not because she had an explicit right to be there.

While many older individuals with PWS may have left the public education system with less than a secondary school completion, most of those now in the system will have the opportunity for 12 or 13 years of public education similar to their peers.

Many gains have been made in the last two decades in the field of special education. In most areas the continuum of educational service begins at the preschool level and continues to the post-secondary level. In urbanized areas there are early-intervention programmes for infants with developmental disabilities that occur before nursery and kindergarten programmes (Mitchell and Brown, 1990). At the other end of the continuum, colleges now have a mandate for the provision of adult special-education programming, creating the possibility of life-long learning opportunities for individuals with special needs.

## The parents' rights

Once parents are compelled to send their children to school, it would be undemocratic to deny access to and control over the process of education (Mackay, 1984). In practice, parents play a meaningful role. In Canada, most school jurisdictions are run by school boards composed of publicly elected citizens. Provision for parent involvement in education is implicit in provincial school acts, ministerial regulations, or school-board policy. Even if parents do not choose to become active participants in education in an organizational sense, they have some rights that enable their fullest participation in the education of their child. Briefly, these generally include the following:

*The right to information*. Parents have the right to access school files. In practice this means access to the file contents in the presence of an educator, who will assist with their interpretation.

*The right to informed consent*. Parents have the right to be fully informed about decisions that have to be made with respect to their child.

*The right to assessment.* Parents may request a psycho-educational assessment in order to determine educational needs. Such assessments are usually handled at the district level, as the testing skills required are usually beyond those of the classroom teacher or learning assistance teacher. (In most districts the right to an independent evaluation is not enunciated. Parents may choose to independently contract for a third-party assessment, however school districts are not bound to adopt the recommendations. In practice, special-education departments will consider the recommendations and implement them as practicable. As the personal credibility of the outside assessor is critical to the acceptance process, parents are advised to consult with special-education administrators before committing themselves to costly services.)

*The right to participate in the individual educational planning (IEP) process.* Standards established under PL 94–142 in the United States included a joint conference between educators and parents, care providers, or guardians, and the client. Participation is more often specified in policy rather than legislation in Canada, and in practice occurs in many, if not most, school jurisdictions.

*The right to appeal.* Parents have the right to appeal decisions, most commonly placement, IEP, or disciplinary decisions. The appeal process is usually outlined in school-board policy, and identifies a hierarchy of personnel to whom to appeal.

*The right to have information released to other professionals.* Parents must sign a 'Consent for Release of Information' form in order to have school-file information released to other professionals. Only pertinent and specific information will be released. This gives parents very specific controls over where and how their child is referred.

Mackay (1984) suggests that 'new procedural rights – whether arising from common-law doctrines of fairness, provincial statutes, or the Charter of Rights – will make the life of school administrators and teachers more complex and more interesting'. It is the parents who are informed of their rights who will be able to challenge the system effectively as they advocate on behalf of their child.

## Special-education services

Special-education supports vary from jurisdiction to jurisdiction. Common services include: psycho-educational assessment, learning assistance, special classes, counselling, physiotherapy, speech/language therapy, and special transportation. Schools also can facilitate vision, hearing, and scoliosis screening. Parents are advised to contact the local special education department office in order to find out what services are available.

Most students with PWS will require some of the supports mentioned above through their school career. Also, it should be understood that the headmaster/mistress is legally responsible for the programme operated within the school, while the district special education department has a responsibility for the monitoring of the quality of programmes.

The PWSA has published a pamphlet titled, 'What educators should know about Prader–Willi syndrome', which lists and explains recommendations for teachers and school personnel (Table 8.2). The message comes from the collective experience of parents and educators, and should be understood by both.

From the experience of the authors, it is also important to inform all school personnel about the syndrome and specifically to bring the identity of an affected child to their attention. Non-teaching personnel such as teacher-aides, janitors, secretaries, and bus-drivers have proved instrumental in effective monitoring within the school and during transit. For example, teacher-aides doing routine playground supervision have prevented food transactions between students; janitors have ensured the quick removal of garbage bins after lunch periods; and secretaries have reported hallway loiterers. It is difficult for bus-drivers to stop the consumption of food, although they can report it and encourage other students to protect their lunches.

Preferably, such personnel would be included in a staff presentation on the syndrome. Simply giving them literature to read without the opportunity for discussion may leave a faulty or incomplete picture. Identifying the PWS student by showing a photograph, rather than simply verbal descriptions, is recommended.

**Table 8.2** What educators should know about Prader–Willi Syndrome

| |
|---|
| Keep the classroom free from any food and/or food-related items. |
| Choose systems of rewards and behavioural management that do not rely on food as a reinforcer. |
| Maintain constant and consistent communication with the family. |
| Plan lessons that are age-appropriate, of high interest, and short duration. |
| Include physical education activities regularly. |
| Provide related services that can enhance self-image, such as speech and language therapy. |
| Offer opportunities for students to work together by sharing classroom responsibilities. |
| Inform other students about PWS. |
| During calm times, encourage exploration of feelings and emotions as a technique for minimizing the temper-tantrums associated with PWS. |

*From* Prader–Willi Syndrome Association, Edina, MN.

## Labelling

Labelling is often misunderstood by parents. Many school districts receive special-education funding based on the categorical approach to the identification of pupils with special-education needs. It is usually necessary for special-education administrators to categorize or attach a label to a child in order to generate funds from the different categories of disability within the fiscal management process. As this is basically a paper-and-pencil activity, parents will not necessarily be aware. Even when a special-needs student is fully integrated into regular classrooms for instruction, labelling may have taken place.

In some cases it is an advantage to be labelled as moderately mentally handicapped as this will generate more funds to the system than being labelled educably mentally handicapped or learning disabled. Even if the child is fully integrated, administrators will seek to include the PWS child in an appropriate category in order to generate funds to provide the other supports that may be required, for example speech and language therapy and extra playground supervision.

As labelling is contingent upon assessment, educators may have their own administrative agenda when asking parental permission for psycho-educational assessment. It may be helpful to know that most special-education administrators do not like this labelling requirement any more than parents do.

By contrast, block-funding is a simple funding mechanism based on a per-student grant, provided to school districts based on the total number of students who are the responsibility of that jurisdiction. In Alberta, the special-education block-funding began in 1984, and the province became non-categorical in its approach. The new Alberta School Act (1988) permits the local boards to determine that a student is in need of special-education services based on a student's behavioural, communicational, intellectual, or physical characteristics, or some combinations of these (Conn-Blowers and McLeod, 1989). The use of such student description is more accommodating of the range of variability and needs within special-needs student populations.

Such details of the fiscal management process are not generally known to parents – the information should be readily available upon request. The movement toward student description is an advantage for PWS parents. Since there is a wide range of intellectual variability within the syndrome, PWS students do not fit neatly into a specific disability category. Some parents have resisted and resented the label of moderate mental handicap, for example, yet the support service required in the educational setting may be greater for the student with PWS than for a student with a moderate mental handicap. Any shift to have service level determined by student need should be supported by PWS parents.

## Individual educational plans

United States Public Law 94–142 (1975) defined the rights of developmentally disabled children, including the right to individualized educational plans. These plans were intended to ensure quality and accountability by those responsible for the education of handicapped children. Minimum standards for an individual plan (Bernstein *et al.*, 1981), included:

- development of a conference involving the student, guardian and professionals concerned;
- formalization in writing of a detailed and individualized programme plan. The content includes:
  - description of the student's conditions and needs;
  - specification of short- and long-term goals;
  - statement of expected timetable for goal attainment;
  - listing of all services to be provided;
  - identification of all service delivery agencies and personnel involved;
  - specification of how services are to be delivered in the normal, or least restrictive, environment;
  - statement of objective criteria and schedules for evaluation;
  - provision for periodic review.

The legislation succeeded in focusing attention on the individual needs of students, but also resulted in requests for programmes that were non-traditional and often costly to school boards.

Influenced by the American precedent, Ontario's Education Act (1980) defined the special-education programme as 'a programme based on and modified by the results of continuous assessment and evaluation, that includes a plan containing specific objectives and an outline of services that meets the needs of the exceptional pupil' (Wilson, 1989). This definition contains characteristics similar to those in PL 94–142; however, while the Act gives parents a statutory right to appeal placement decisions and pupil identification issues, it does not give them the right to appeal the content of the curriculum, the provision of services, or the nature of the programme (Wilson *et al.*, 1989). Other provinces have opted for the inclusion of individualized education planning provisions within policy at the provincial level rather than statutory inclusion. Regardless of whether contained in policy or statute, the influence of PL 94–142 is indisputable.

In practice most guidelines for IEP writing include the elements outlined above. Current practice as evidenced in Canadian educational literature suggests that the concept of individualized education plans for special-needs students is universally embraced.

While the concept may be contained within policy, its application is not always consistent. IEPs vary widely in content and quality. Some PWS parents have reported intimate involvement in the IEP process; others have only been called in after the fact to ratify educator's intents; still others have been unaware of their right to participate in the IEP process, or aware of the IEP document. It should be obvious that the right to an IEP does not guarantee its effectiveness. If concerned about the level of involvement or the adequacy of process, parents are advised to contact the administrator in charge of special education to clarify local policy.

**Integration**

The legal basis for integration in Canada is rooted in The Canadian Charter of Rights and Freedoms (Government of Canada, 1984). Section 15(1) says, in part:

> Every individual is equal before and under the law and has the right to the equal protection and equal benefit of the law without discrimination and, in particular, without discrimination based on race, national or ethnic origin, colour, religion, sex, age or mental or physical disability.

Consistent with the intent of the Charter, the School Regulations and Minister of Education Orders (Government of British Columbia, 1989), which accompany the most recently adopted School Act in Canada, that of the province of British Columbia, state that:

> Unless the educational needs of a handicapped student indicate that the student's educational program should be provided otherwise, a board shall provide that student with an educational program in classrooms where that student is integrated with other students who do not have handicaps (Minister's Order 13/89).

Hence, school boards that have not already adopted local policies consistent with the direction of integration will now be required to do so. The British Columbia situation is not unique, but rather reflects the generally changing nature of social policy toward those with handicaps and disabilities.

Most Canadian PWS parents known to the authors support the principle of integration. Depending on the degree of disability and the supervision requirements, however, some would prefer a more segregated environment. While larger school jurisdictions may be able to run a dual-track system, that is to say, offering opportunities for both integrated and segregated placements, most smaller jurisdictions will have less scope for options. Younger parents in particular must therefore acknowledge the process of integration, as it is a reality in today's educational system.

## Teacher/parent communications

Effective communications are necessary in order to serve the best interests of the PWS child. Communication, however, is a two-way process and is often clouded by other agenda. From the parents' perspective there may be initial uncertainty as to how much information to communicate to teachers about PWS. The mother of one child receiving a diagnosis in the primary years hesitated, saying,

> . . . too often children get labelled. If I was to tell her teacher that she had PWS, I feel that she would go straight to the library and pick out probably the medical dictionary that I did when I first found out, and all it says is 'incessant weight gain and mental retardation', and I don't want her labelled that way.

On the other hand, another mother receiving a diagnosis at about the same age declared,

> I immediately took the letter to the school that very same day that I got it in order that they could start benefitting from knowing that at school. I mean it was important to get that to school.

In the first case, the parent hesitated about sharing the diagnosis for fear of the labelling that would take place. The usual argument is that a label becomes a self-fulfilling prophecy: the child will become what is defined by the label as teachers look for the characteristics they have been told to expect, or will segregate the child in some way. Without the label, teachers might give the child more objective treatment. By contrast, in the second example the parent was eager to share the diagnostic information with the teachers in the hope that it would help to explain behaviours and learning difficulties, and aid in better intervention.

Understandably, the subjectivity of the parenting experience can interfere with the ability to communicate information objectively. Educators have been critical of parents who come across as over-protective, demanding, unrealistic, antagonistic, uncooperative, and emotional. Understanding the educational system beforehand will help a parent not to be intimidated at the time of critical interviews and conferences. Taking along an advocate who is knowledgeable about PWS can be helpful, particularly if parents are anticipating a difficult situation or feel the need for the support of a third party to discuss ideas after the meeting. Members of a local or provincial PWS parent association can assist here. Older parents have likely had similar experiences, and are committed to the needs of the PWS child and family, yet can add objectivity and equilibrium. Professional advocates can also be helpful, though it is essential that the atmosphere of the meeting be set by the parents' style, with advice from the advocate. The private consultant should have a working knowledge of the school system as well as previous experience with PWS.

When pursuing additional educational supports for a PWS child it is imperative to be well-organized and prepared. Care should be taken to pre-plan the questions that need to be asked, particularly regarding process; to amplify the historic record of the child with information that might not exist in the school file; to provide literature ('expert opinion') that supports the position taken; to acknowledge the fiscal and staffing limitations of the system; and to articulate clearly what is being requested.

From the educators' perspective, care must be taken not to intimidate parents. By virtue of their educational level and apparent control over the decision-making process, this is a real possibility. Parents have related the frustrations of not being able to get satisfaction from special-education administrators, for example. In a district committed to full integration of all special-needs students, parents were told that a teacher-aide would not be supplied to the classroom of their PWS child. The parents found themselves thwarted and communication ended. They resorted to private consultation outside of the district, and were encouraged to make an enquiry through the ministry of education. In another situation, a single parent, feeling blocked in trying to get recess and lunch-hour supervision, took a similar route to an outside consultant in order to educate the headmaster to the realities of PWS needs.

Almost without exception educators have been found to be receptive to information about PWS. Passing on printed information is an important means of communication. Printed materials and videotapes have the advantage of objectivity, and appeal to the academic nature of professionals. Most educators will not have had experience with PWS, and will readily acknowledge that parents are the real experts. Aggressiveness, on the other hand, may put teachers and administrators on the defensive. Some of these will subscribe to the philosophy that the best defence is sometimes a good offence, thus contributing to a cycle of impaired communication.

Parents are encouraged to keep a log of contacts with the school and other service systems. Names, dates, and the content of telephone conversations, interviews, and correspondence should be kept dutifully. Assessment reports can be requested for personal files. When the outcomes of meetings can potentially lead to problems, parents should follow up with a note to the other party summarizing the understanding reached, if this is not forthcoming from the other party. This helps to clarify areas of misunderstanding as soon as possible, and documents important decisions that may have been made even on an informal basis. It will also bring a degree of objectivity to the communication process, which all too frequently is clouded by emotion.

## Educational jurisdictions

In Canada, education is a provincial responsibility. Hence legislation governing the operation of education varies from province to province. Within provinces, local school jurisdictions set policies consistent with the legislation of the various provincial ministries of education regulations and guidelines. The Canadian education system appears, both legislatively and in educational practice, to lie between those of England and the United States. In England there are Local Education Authorities and they receive their authority and legislation from central government through the Department of Education and Science. In Canada and England, there are provisions for special schools, and in both countries parents have the right to appeal against local school board or education authority decisions over placement. This is in contrast to the United States where the federal Education for All Handicapped Children Act (PL 94–142) of 1975 mandated that public education had the responsibility for the mainstreaming of all handicapped children and set the standards for this. The American national standards can consequently be objectively adjudicated by judicial process.

From a national perspective, in Canada there are obvious differences in the delivery of special-education services. Regional or provincial disparities do exist. Gall (1984), in discussing these disparities, points out that some provinces took the route of mandatory legislation, where free and appropriate education was provided to all students without any exclusionary provisions. Others, however, chose permissive legislation that established the concept of educational rights as a favour or privilege and permitted exclusion of special-needs children. With the enactment of the equality rights section (Section 15) of the Canadian Charter of Rights and Freedoms in 1985, however, changes are occurring. As we enter the 1990s, eight provinces have legislation protecting the welfare rights of exceptional children to an education (Goguen, 1989). The evolution is toward a more homogeneous approach to special-education opportunities across Canada, although there are some current conflicts clearly identified by Csapo.

## GOVERNMENT SOCIAL SERVICES

Social services in Canada have been changing during the last few years. In an effort to improve fiscal responsibility, bureaucracies have been decreased and contracted services have increased in many jurisdictions. Non-profit societies and private enterprisers have received government contracts to provide social services. Social services thus has become a complex system that can be very confusing to parents unaccustomed to receiving 'hand-outs'. Indeed, parental pride and attitudes towards social dependency can further hamper access to needed supports.

## Services

Many parents take advantage of government-subsidized programmes such as infant stimulation, preschool development centres, and respite care when their PWS child is very young. Accessibility to programmes, however, is sometimes an issue. One mother of a two-year-old stated with disgust that, 'due to budget restraints we couldn't get into the infant stimulation programme'. Unfortunately, contracted services are for limited numbers of clients, and are not guaranteed beyond the length of the contract.

Social services frequently seem to be subject to fiscal restraint, creating further uncertainty for long-term planning. Most adults with PWS receive a handicap pension and may additionally utilize residential placement or treatment facilities. In some cases, there are extensions to basic financial supports based on extraordinary costs associated with treatment and care. Existing services, however, do not meet the needs of every family situation. A father of a difficult-to-manage young man of 21 years resented the lack of support from social services when he approached them for assistance:

> We were told there was no money. 'Get a volunteer,' he said. Nothing like, 'Let's see if we can get you a volunteer'. Just straightforward, 'get a volunteer'.

This situation was not unique to the one family. A second set of parents with a 22-year-old PWS daughter complained about the same department, saying, 'they are a stumbling block really . . . the greatest problem that we have encountered in the 22 years of having her.'

It appears that the local interpretation of provincial policy in this particular district was restrictive from the parents' perspective. Given that both families were dealing with the same social worker, this might be viewed as a unique situation. It does illustrate, however, one of the difficulties in social services delivery. The interpretation of policies and regulations are often at the discretion of field-workers who may have little experience with PWS, and perhaps even little interest in 'sticking their neck out' to be creative in interpreting and applying policy.

## Access to services

Common difficulties expressed by parents include: a lack of knowledge about what is available; a lack of compassion on the part of government employees; a lack of funds available to support the request; and inflexibility of eligibility criteria and guidelines for expenditures. Thus, the manner and degree of assistance provided either modifies or augments parental stresses. There do not seem to be any differences between rural and urban service provision; rather, service seems to depend more on the knowledge of PWS by the key worker.

Recent applications of technology may assist parents to access information more easily in some areas. The development of communication centres such as the Alberta Response Centre, aim to answer parents directly, or within 24 hours, by the use of telephone and computer information networks (Disability Information System of Canada – DISC). There is every sign that such procedures will be extremely helpful to individuals, families, and agencies in the future.

## The importance of documentation

It is important to document all aspects of PWS development and services utilized. Documentation becomes increasingly important with age when trying to obtain services. Child records should include details of the following:

Weight
Hospitalizations
Medications

Respite services used
Assessments
Treatment programmes
Education and training
Use of specialized medical, educational, or social services

Anecdotal information highlighting developmental sequalae are also important. The use of commercially available books on child development, including baby and school-year books can be very helpful.

Human-services planners are often concerned with generic issues rather than syndrome-specific concerns; they may be able to justify very little time for low-incidence conditions such as PWS. Since there is not yet a well-understood progression within the syndrome in the context of our present human services, cases will likely be dealt with on an *ad hoc* basis.

Without documentation, parents are placing a great deal of trust in the professional judgement of a social worker – one who may never have had the opportunity to work with PWS previously. However, many of the behaviours of a social and educational nature are amenable to general interventions. Although there are case-specific concerns, general principles are now recognized by many educationalists and psychologists within the context of variability. It must be emphasized that parents are the major source of information on variability – it is to them that professionals must turn to gain the necessary information about the idiosyncracies of a particular child. Although it may be difficult, parents who have documented this information in writing in advance are more likely to get a positive response from knowledgeable professionals.

## THE MULTIDISCIPLINARY TEAM

This refers to the disciplines that are involved as part of a team in addressing the needs of an individual with PWS – a group of professionals who collaborate in order to come up with a 'game plan' for the individual of concern.

## Team make-up

Who the team includes will vary from case to case, depending on the subject's age of development and the agencies involved. The initial team is usually a hospital group composed primarily of clinical staff. The focus of this team is diagnosis and infant health care. Once the baby leaves the hospital the team-focus is on infant development. At this stage the team may be co-ordinated under the auspices of an infant-stimulation programme or child-development centre programme. Medical specialists now generally reduce their involvement, while nurses, and physio- and occupational-therapists play an increasingly important role. Early-childhood educators begin to take a more prominent role. By the school years, educators generally have the primary concerns, and often assume responsibility for service co-ordination. Special classes, learning assistance, counselling, speech and language therapy, adapted physical education, and special transportation are some of the educational supports that may be necessary, and these may involve various educators including psychologists. By the adult years, the shift is to vocational and community-living concerns. Team co-ordination is often supplied through social workers or other community-based rehabilitation practitioners involved with the young adult.

Teams are dynamic in that they change membership according to the developmental needs of the child. The team-approach to case management has been described by Greenswag and Alexander (1988). Their text on the management of Prader–Willi syndrome is an excellent resource for multidisciplinary involvement. At its best the team becomes interdisciplinary, that is to say, the personnel share their interdisciplinary knowledge, but different team members may take over depending on their personal knowledge of the child and their availability. This approach can help to reduce the number of professionals a family sees on a regular basis. Unfortunately, the model is not yet commonplace.

## Short- and long-term planning

The purpose of the multidisciplinary team is to develop comprehensive assessment and management strategies. Parents should be prepared to participate fully in long-range and short-term goal-setting, approval of intervention strategies, and methodological approaches.

The terminology for the master plan varies according to the discipline, and is commonly referred to by initials. There is little difference in intent between an individual education plan (IEP) and an individual programme plan (IPP). The former is the preferred term within an educational setting, while the latter is common among social and vocational services programmes. A general service plan (GSP) is a master action plan, often co-ordinating at a community level a number of agency involvements, but which assumes IPPs or IEPs at the level of individual agencies. An individual transition plan (ITP) delineates the plan for the gradual transition from one setting, agency, or programme to another.

There are no universally prescribed formats for these plans, although each type has some common elements. Some agencies, or districts, however, may choose to standardize formats within their sphere of operation. The intent of all plans is to document in a comprehensive fashion the agreed upon programme for the individual. The individualized plan will also identify a case manager, the person assigned responsibility for monitoring implementation of the plan. Some further comments on the development of IPPs are given in the next chapter.

## The case manager

Parents interact with the multidisciplinary team in two ways: either as a member of the group at IEP meetings, or as individuals in the day-to-day operation of the programme. As some team members may be itinerant in some settings, it may be difficult for parents to maintain communication as regularly as they might like with all of them. There is usually one primary worker, however, who is designated as the case manager or team leader who should co-ordinate activities and maintain contact. The designation of this key individual is routinely made at the initial IEP meeting.

### Parent participation

Following the passage of PL 94–142 in the United States, which established minimum standards for the writing of individualized programme plans, parents' participation in educational decision-making became more popular as the law required parent or guardian input into a planning conference. As mentioned earlier in Canada there seems to be an implicit right for parents to participate in the education of their child. Since parents are compelled by law to send their children to school, they have a corresponding right to participate in the educational process. They are not, however, required by law to attend school planning meetings. The requirement for parent participation may be contained within ministerial regulation or policy of the school jurisdiction, placing the onus upon the educators to ensure that parents have the opportunity for involvement. In addition to the right to participate in decision-making on behalf of their child, parents usually have the right to appeal placement decisions, and the right to access file information.

Some parents have reported feeling out of place, unwelcomed, intimidated, or discouraged by the multidisciplinary team. This may be particularly true for parents unaccustomed to working in professional environments. The problem can be exacerbated when the team focus does not coincide with parent needs. The team may be the only sounding board for the parent who is struggling with day-to-day management problems; their agenda, therefore, may be broader than the interests or mandate of the team. At the secondary school level, for example, the team may be primarily composed of personnel from educationally related disciplines, whose mandate is to focus on education and transition planning. Medically related issues, while of peripheral importance, may not receive the airing the parent is seeking. Parents often need support and advice on how to work within the other systems, and seek such support during team participation. While the purpose of the team is to support the PWS child, a holistic approach to child needs usually incorporates an opportunity for the expression of all parent concerns.

## PWS PARENT ASSOCIATIONS

Because of the low incidence of PWS, there are few parent organizations in Canada. Most have been organized as provincial groups, although there are a few local chapters emerging. Some, such as the Alberta PWS Association, have incorporated as a non-profit society; others exist essentially as mutual support groups. Indeed, the history of most groups is that of a banding together of parents with common concerns to support each other, particularly with respect to emotional needs. Advocacy, education, and lobbying have been part of a natural evolution, enabling parents to operate within the various ecological environments or systems discussed in this chapter.

### Membership activities

Activities undertaken by any group will depend on local circumstances. In general terms, groups seem to focus on mutual support in order to improve the lives of individuals with PWS and their families. Pragmatically, this often involves personal support, advocacy on behalf of those in need, public education about the syndrome, pursuit of programmes and facilities, and the support of research.

Personal support is probably the primary function. Often it is nothing more than an empathetic ear, or the giving of advice as to how to proceed or where to go for resources. For those receiving the support, however, it can be an answer to a prayer. A young parent of a three year old was given the name of the local association president by the doctor, and had this to say:

> We phoned and talked to her for about half an hour about it. She explained it more . . . she was very co-operative, very nice. You know, she had a listening ear. She told me about her little girl. She has a PW little girl . . . that was basically where we got our support from.

Monthly meetings, guest speakers, summer camps, and family retreats are all intended to support the needs of parents. Advocacy can occur at all levels of service delivery. Association members have advocated for others during times of crisis with respect to vocational and residential services, and with the school system in pursuit of more appropriate levels of support. Public education can take many forms, such as the dissemination of literature to hospitals, medical clinics, health units, and other allied health offices. The Lower Mainland PWS Association co-operated with a local cable-TV station in the production of a special feature on the syndrome. Other local associations have been able to obtain media coverage in order to promote public awareness. In Calgary, Alberta, the association president and his family have had the opportunity to address medical school interns. Of course, education is also the motivation for a conference: the Ontario PWS Association sponsors an annual provincial conference on PWS, and the Alberta association undertook to host the thirteenth annual conference of the PWS Association of America.

The Canadian associations are not a primary source of funds for research purposes, but they have been supportive in facilitating research. Indeed, the research reported in parts of this text is a testimony to the commitment of western Canadian PWS associations to support research.

Some parents choose not to participate in association meetings as a result of negative experiences. In such cases, personal stress is usually such that listening to the problems of others is found to be exacerbating. If meetings become nothing more than an occasion for the venting of feelings and personal problem-solving, the association will be at risk. Where parents have the opportunity for positive involvement and are united in a common cause, there is more likely to be commitment. It is impossible, however, to meet the needs of all members at all times.

## The Canadian network

At present there is an emerging Canadian network of parents and professionals concerned with PWS. While there is no formalized national body, networking occurs among the provincial and local associations, which is encouraging. The *PWS Newsletter–Canada* distributes information on PWS from coast to coast. As with all newsletters that rely on volunteer labour and donations, it is published somewhat irregularly, two or three times annually. It does, however, feature Canadian content. Perhaps the most significant event contributing to the coalescing of a Canadian PWS identity was the hosting of the 13th Annual Conference of the PWS Association of America in Calgary, Alberta, in July 1989. This was the first time that the conference was held outside the United States, an acknowledgement that Canada had the professional and parent resources to be able to organize the prestigious event herself. The informal networking among Canadian participants, and the media coverage received were important factors contributing to the establishment of a Canadian PWS identity.

### The PWS Association of America (PWSA)

The PWSA was founded in Seattle, Washington in 1975. By year end 1976, membership had grown to 140 parents and professionals, including representation from Canada, England, Australia, Norway, and Germany. In 1980 a system of officially incorporated chapters was established to link the many groups of parents that had begun to meet regionally. There were 27 such groups in the United States by 1990.

A major function of the PWSA is that of a national clearinghouse for the dissemination of information about PWS. Indeed, this organization functions internationally in this regard. The PWSA publication, 'The Gathered View', is a twelve-page, bimonthly publication linking PWS parents and those serving them. The overall goals of the association include: improving communications; advocacy for affected individuals; support for research and the development of a national centre for services; normalization of life for affected children and their families; and encouragement of interdependent relationships between parents and professionals (Wett, 1988).

Many Canadian PWS parents have affiliated with the PWSA, and enjoy the various benefits of the organization. The yearly conference of the PWSA has become an annual holiday for some families, particularly those who have been members of the Association for some years. They look forward to the support of old friends, and the opportunity to keep abreast of recent PWS developments. For those with PWS, whether child or adult, there is also the opportunity to renew friendships during the youth activities programme, a three-day schedule of well-supervised activities.

## SUMMARY

Chapter 8 has examined family coping according to ecological contexts or the systems and environments in which parents have to exist. Included are essential service systems such as medical, educational, and government social services, as well as less-formal systems, such as the neighbourhood and PWS parent associations.

- PWS family stress is often associated with such systemic factors as the lack of knowledgeable professionals; the number of professionals involved; the lack of understanding of system dynamics; changing policies and procedures; rigidity of policy interpretation; and communication breakdowns. Professionals, often working in isolation from each other, are not always sensitive to such systemic pressures placed on families.
- The systems within which PWS families operate in Canada have been influenced by the philosophy of normalization, and aim to provide optimal opportunities within a community context. Consistent with the opportunities available to all of us, there should be a range of options for those with PWS as well.
- The lack of awareness of PWS among agency personnel is understandable, given the low incidence of the disorder. Professional and public awareness is the joint responsibility of professional groups and parent associations.
- Parents are not always well informed or knowledgeable about their rights regarding professional service delivery systems. They are often overwhelmed by the system dynamics or intimidated by individual professionals. Parents become empowered through their association with self-advocacy groups.
- Within government social services, funding is not always available for children and families in need. Due to rigid interpretation of policies, PWS children do not necessarily meet

the criteria for particular funding. This does not make their needs any the less urgent. Classification of a child as learning disabled in some jurisdictions, for example, may mean that the child is not eligible for certain special services despite an obvious need. It must be recognized that such label-laden judgements make little sense in terms of social service or educational delivery. It is the individual needs of the child, established through assessment and observation, which should determine service levels. For this reason, individualized funding represents a possible solution. Parents require low-cost support in a variety of forms.

- Professionals inexperienced with PWS must be cautious not to dismiss the PWS parent as simply over-anxious. The prolonged burden of caring, the intensity of stress associated with daily child management, and frustrations associated with advocacy with service delivery systems, can have a debilitating effect on parent morale, health, and marital relationships.
- Parents need to know what types of questions to ask professionals, and the questions they are likely to be asked in return. Brochures and hand-outs produced by the Prader–Willi Syndrome Association and other parent groups can be very helpful in this regard. Parents are encouraged to write down their questions in advance of important meetings, and to bring another person along for personal support and advocacy if necessary.
- The principles of normalization dictate integrated, community-based experiences for those with handicaps. Structure and supervision, however, become both philosophically and pragmatically difficult in the community. With PWS, perhaps more than with many other syndromes, there is a distinct need for structure. Parents must begin to teach their children to accept structures at an early age. PWS children do not generally respond well to a *laissez-faire* atmosphere, or to parents weak on organization, patience, and discipline.
- In order to be good advocates for their child within service systems, parents need to be well-informed. Membership in provincial, national, or international PWS associations ensures access to current research information, as well as to a network of parental supports. Such affiliation is particularly

important for parents in rural environments, who might not have the immediate support of knowledgeable professionals or experienced parents.

*Chapter 9*

# Quality of life

Quality-of-life issues are becoming increasingly important in relation to disability, and hold particular interest for those working with PWS. Much of the early work was done in the field of developmental disabilities, but in the last 20 years, research workers and practitioners have also written about quality of life in the fields of physical disability, ageing, and mental health.

One of the present authors has recently completed a longitudinal study of 240 adolescents and adults and their quality of life (Brown *et al.*, 1989). The individuals had developmental disabilities, with a few suffering from PWS. Because of this, a substudy was undertaken with the help of the first author examining a small group of 12 people with PWS. The aims were to explore the concerns of these individuals and their families; to look at the similarities with others who have different disabilities; and to discuss some of the practical implications arising from a study of quality of life. This chapter examines the conceptual bases of quality-of-life studies, and discusses the recent work of the authors in this area.

## A DEFINITION

As used here, quality of life refers to the discrepancy between a person's achieved and unmet needs and desires. This definition assumes a discrepancy model: the greater the discrepancy the poorer the quality of life. The extent to which an individual increasingly controls aspects of life reflects the quality of life, regardless of original baseline assessment (Brown *et al.*, 1989). Many authors seem to hold similar views, and models of quality of life have been developed by a number of people (Borthwick-

Duffy, 1986; Parmenter, 1988; Schalock, 1988). The key concepts in these models involve the following:

- A holistic view of rehabilitation, that is, taking account of all aspects of the individual's life: education, vocation, social living, home living, and leisure and recreational involvement.
- A case manager who knows the client very well, works with the individual within his or her own environment, and is able to draw upon the resources of many professionals.
- An examination of the individual's thoughts and feelings about him or herself and all aspects of life. Often these views are very private, and therefore must include confidentiality and consent of the individual to release information. This is normally given, and it is therefore possible to discuss most aspects of lifestyle within the family context. Indeed, the perception of the individual about personal-life progress, needs, and worries constitute the major component of any rehabilitation.
- The element of choice is essential. The individual must be in a position to make personal choices about life, education, vocation, and so on. This has been used in a variety of situations with a range of people who have various disabilities – yet this criterion raises a major concern when considered within the field of PWS.

  Many choices surround the issue of eating behaviours; it is therefore important to stress that choices should not be permitted if they involve significant harm to the individual. The determination of significance, of course, is usually a subjective decision, and one with which the parents need to feel comfortable. A better way of looking at the situation is to accept the choices that are made, but enable the individual with PWS to obtain or modify personal goals through highly structured and careful programming of rehabilitation. An important aspect of choice is that it empowers people the moment others accept that they are saying what they want, since acceptance adds positively to self-image and personal dignity. These, in turn, tend to build confidence which can lead to action.
- The development of positive self-concepts and powerful forces of motivation, which enable the individual to

commence the process of rehabilitation. In several important studies (Borthwick-Duffy, 1986; Brown *et al.*, 1989; Goode, 1988; Parmenter, 1988; Schalock, 1988) these have proved to be key factors in rehabilitation, and may be even greater than traditional procedures, which regard learning-specific skills as very potent. Such skill training is necessary, but the primary issues are choice, development of self-image, and empowerment of the individual, which eventually enable him or her to organize his or her life according to personal wishes. Development of such a process can be time-consuming, at times frustrating, and makes rehabilitation more complex. Until recently, many of the procedures carried out in rehabilitation have been directed at ensuring that the individual is quiet and peaceful so that other people can get on with their own lives. Effective rehabilitation recognizes that individuals who become empowered and self-confident also make heavy demands on those around them.

## THE DEVELOPMENT OF A MODEL

The development of a model of quality of life involves some key issues and ways of thinking. Table 9.1 represents some of the major components.

It should be stressed that perceptions by the individual are critical. For example, the perception of feeling well may be more important to behaviour than actually being well. Feeling safe in an environment may have more impact than feeling unsafe though physically protected. This raises a range of issues concerning personal perception and choice. Most people are concerned with the physical issues of safety, but it is now recognized that although this may save individuals from accidents, it may also result in delayed psychological and social development. Thus the individual is psychologically and socially at risk. It is the interplay of these three areas that often causes some of the major concerns in rehabilitation for parents and practitioners, who often choose physical safety while letting psychological and social factors limit the individual's experience. The reasons for such choices often relate to fear of harm,

**Table 9.1** Model of quality-of-life variables for handicapped people

| |
|---|
| *Subjective evaluation* |
| Perceived growth and mastery |
| Safety and security |
| Social involvement and feelings of belonging |
| Independence/control |
| Responsibility |
| Self-esteem |
| Expectation |
| Perceived goal attainment |
| Perceived supports |
| Satisfaction level |
| Perceived health (mental and physical) |
| Normalcy of life |
| Pace of life |
| Family stability |
| *Objective evaluation* |
| Skill attainment |
| Physical environment |
| Level of integration (physical and social) |
| Leisure activities |
| Training plans |
| Actual support systems |
| Income |
| Possessions |
| Health |
| Philosophy of training agencies |
| Attitudes of training staff |
| Attitudes of community |

Brown *et al.* (1989).

problems over insurance, and legal or professional vulnerability (Goldenberg, 1990).

## LABELLING

It is important for parents to have an accurate diagnosis of PWS. It is argued, however, that the label itself may result in other secondary handicaps, and in some instances may be more problematic than the original condition. It has become quite common to associate PWS with a number of other conditions, such as low intelligence, aggressive behaviour, problems concerning sexuality, attention, and motor skills, to mention but a few.

Although these may be part of a cluster of behaviours around PWS, they also may occur, or be increased, because of social attitudes and preconceived ideas. This is the case in many conditions associated with cognitive disability, and in recent years it has been recognized that by reducing a reaction to a label, more effective rehabilitation can take place. For example, the diagnosis of PWS may have major significance from medical and biochemical perspectives. On the other hand, it may have little relevance for psychological and social interventions, which have to be directed toward aspects of performance shown by a particular individual.

One of the characteristics of quality-of-life studies is that they have demonstrated that individuals with PWS, among other conditions, show an enormous range of behavioural skills. It is apparent that some people with PWS can live in the community very effectively; that some do not seem restricted in terms of intelligence; and that some are able to maintain themselves in employment. Although these may not be common features of people with PWS, the very fact that they exist raises the question of how one can modify the environment of people with PWS to capitalize on positive features, and enable the individuals and their families to function as optimally as possible.

## THE FAMILY IN QUALITY-OF-LIFE STUDIES

In examining the quality of life of people with PWS, it is necessary to accept from the outset that there is an extreme burden facing parents. Although there are those who look to institutionalization and residential care for long-term solutions, there is no strong evidence that if provided with such environments PWS people do better in terms of quality of life than those who remain with their families or in the community. Indeed, there is considerable practical evidence to suggest the opposite. However, if they are to live in the community, then respite care is necessary. The inability of parents to go on holiday, to respond to the needs of their partners and to their other children makes it essential that support services be provided away from home, from time to time, or by someone moving into the home environment.

As mentioned earlier, because of the type of care that can now be provided and the structures available for managing eating behaviours, it is likely that many of those with PWS will live well into their adult years. It can be expected that longevity will be extended further as knowledge and experience increases. For these reasons, issues that have not been confronted by most PWS parents to date will become matters of some importance. Issues related to sexuality are bound to become more common, not necessarily because of the behaviour of the individual, but because they will mix with peers who themselves are sexually inquisitive. Earlier in the book some of the issues associated with schooling and eating behaviours were described. This was seen as a major difficulty for many PWS children, but the same issues arise when individuals obtain work in the community, unless counselling and advice is given to those in the environment in which the individual is to work. Issues relating to vocational training and employment will continue to emerge as long-term demands for jobs and day-programmes increase. Certainly, concerns relating to the ageing process will need to be addressed in the future as well.

There is no single answer that is suitable for all families with PWS dependants. There are families that may see in some of these recommendations something that is unsuitable for their situation. The point is that it is wise to consider a wide range of possibilities that try to encompass some of the variations found in individual families with PWS.

## Leisure

Leisure issues are important in quality-of-life studies. It is apparent that much of the leisure skills of those with handicapping conditions are severely attenuated. Some researchers have suggested this is a major reason for the development of secondary handicaps later in life, which look as though they are part of an original syndrome but in fact are added later partly because there are restrictions over leisure-time opportunity and development (Brown *et al.*, 1989; Beck-Ford and Brown, 1984; Day, 1988). Leisure-time activities have a number of components; Nash (1953) suggested four areas:

- Observation or non-participatory leisure activities, such as watching television.
- Social activities, where individuals carry out leisure activities with other people.
- Physical activities.
- Self-actualizing or self-development behaviours.

Although there is considerable overlap among these areas, children tend to move from one type to another. Although there is probably never an equal amount of time spent in each activity, handicapped people tend to have rather fewer skills in the last two than in the first two.

Appropriate leisure activity seems to be very relevant to the development of positive self-image, gross and fine motor-skill development, physical stamina and health, and adequate motivation. Balanced leisure activity can also lead to the development of appropriate social behaviours and planning skills. It is in the development of these areas, and what may be called the 'self-starting' of such behaviours, that PWS children and adults have great difficulty. Unless these attributes are successfully developed, notwithstanding improvement in current health practices resulting in greater longevity, the chances of obtaining competitive employment and positive social development are likely to be restricted.

Another aspect of quality of life that is important is the participation in age-appropriate activities and environments, and the use of age-appropriate materials and clothing. Quality-of-life issues cannot be adequately measured unless attention is paid to all aspects of the environment in which the individual lives and develops.

All of the above suggest it is necessary to begin to make use of a much wider range of rehabilitation activities in the leisure domain than has been done to date. Such areas as fine arts must also be stressed; the importance of drama, painting, and music, for example, as important components in the alleviation of certain behaviours and in the development of appropriate skills, can be easily overlooked (Warren, 1989). Indeed, many people with handicaps appear to receive considerable relief from some of the stressful aspects of their symptomatology by involvement in such areas.

## INDIVIDUALIZED PROGRAMME PLANNING

The concept of individualized programme-planning is integral to a quality-of-life model. Very often, the development of individualized procedures, although recognizing the individuality of development, may be abused in the way they are used within school, rehabilitation settings, and the family. Frequently, a wide range of assessment is employed, and individuals are often subjected to meetings or the co-ordination of programmes among a large number of staff.

It is contended that this is a misunderstanding of the individualization process, and does not reflect issues raised from the perspective of quality of life. For example, it seems to be more appropriate for a single-case manager to work with the individual and the family. The goals having been set in general terms, the case manager sets out to develop, with the assistance of colleagues, the procedures that will be necessary to implement programmes. It is critical, however, that the initial goals are once again discussed with the consumer and the family in the context of procedure. One important aspect of counselling in this situation is to encourage the acceptance of the client-chosen goals, and to find ways to implement them that are acceptable to others who live with, or are responsible for, the client. Very often this is a difficult process. At times there are parents who say, 'choice is all very well, but we know that handicapped people are not capable of choice', or there are teachers and other professionals who say that individuals change their mind, or are not consistent in the choice selection.

Variation is a notable feature of all human behaviour. It is suggested that it is only when people have the experience of attempting various choices that learning can be readily modified. People must be able to put forward choices and express their needs. Only then do they feel that they are being taken seriously in terms of their behaviour. From this, more positive self-image and motivation may develop, which is critical to the rehabilitation process. Obviously, to mediate this process requires great skill and experience on the part of the case manager, particularly when it occurs in the client's home or community environment. Understanding, tolerance, and advice, as well as help from parents and others who are involved, are crucial. Undoubtedly, some parents will not be able to follow through with such procedures. Also, it is recognized that many professionals feel their professional role is at stake when they are in such dynamic situations, and in such close proximity to the family. However, for many people, including PWS clients, individualized programme-planning has been a very important aspect of rehabilitation and has often proved successful (Brown *et al.*, 1991).

## THE QUESTIONNAIRES

It was noted above that personal and subjective opinions are important in carrying out a quality-of-life study. For this reason, Brown and Bayer (1991) developed a questionnaire looking at the individual's perception in most domains of life. This has been employed on at least 300 people, and has proved to be beneficial in clinical as well as in research areas.

Research studies (Brown *et al.*, 1989) show that even though people may be of low levels of intelligence, they have been able to express their views clearly and accurately in response to many of the questions. Their range of answers suggests they are very clear about areas in which they are making progress in school and rehabilitation centres. They know the issues that worry and concern them, and the areas in which they are failing; they show remarkably good perception of how they are progressing, and the challenges that confront them. Because the results are as accurate as with other objective criteria, it seems important to take their views into account around a wide range of issues. Further, they provide a wealth of information that is frequently not available from parents, nor from others who work with the clients.

On a number of occasions parents have corrected their own

statements after hearing the comments of their children. Sometimes these involve practical issues of choice or need, or the skills that the individual has or has not gained. There are instances where parents have indicated that individuals have been in control of simple finances, only to have the individual contradict this and say they do not handle money. In one example, the individual did have his own bank account, but the parent made deposits into the account and the individual had never seen the cheques, let alone handled them.

Such lack of opportunity is a critical consideration in designing effective rehabilitation programmes. It is also important that the case manager has accurate and specific information. There are similar examples of how self-esteem can be curtailed and motivation lost. It is not always appropriate to put all finances in an individual's control, but it is important to enable people to be aware of how their actions influence perceptions, and therefore the development of the individual in their care. Such issues abound and can be effectively used in counselling and planning, but it requires close involvement in the family environment by a highly skilled worker who is accepted by the family.

## QUESTIONNAIRE RESULTS

This part of the chapter provides some commentary on the responses made by individuals with PWS. At certain points comments are also made in relation to the much larger sample of individuals who had other forms of mental handicap or disability.

In the case of PWS, the questionnaire was filled in very accurately in relation to food and meals. Individuals are clearly aware of their eating habits (what they eat, do not eat, when they eat, when they should not eat). The questionnaire was given to adolescents and young adults, and although the PWS sample does not represent a comprehensive study, the views are in most cases corroborated by commentary from parents and from the large sample of other individuals with different forms of handicap.

It is important to recognize that there was great variation in responses. PWS people are very different from one another. This makes it difficult to provide general guidance about specific needs. Each case must be treated on an individual basis within the context of family.

The results also indicate that some individuals relied on the agencies they attended, but others were only too delighted to get away from them, recognizing them as restricting places where they felt unhappy, or as not offering training they wanted. As in the major study, several of the parents commented on the value of the questionnaire. Very often it enabled them to highlight or pinpoint issues that were of concern that had not been clarified before. Some indicated that the questionnaire enabled them to formulate the questions they will in future ask agencies and service providers.

The majority of clients saw their lives improving in the future. Such optimism was not always reflected in the parents' views, but it was certainly one of the important aspects of responses from individuals. Most of them, however, anticipated no major change in their skills levels. These were often very simple, such as money handling, food management, clothing choices and budgeting. Similar types of responses indicate that poor learning occurred in many tasks within the larger sample, and that subjects were accurate in relation to objective scores on skills that were measured. Such personal views reflect the way PWS people feel about themselves. Lack of improvement in skills is generally not a fixed feature of the individual so much as a demonstration of the lack of opportunity and choice in the environment. Individuals are not consciously aware of this and attribute lack of progress to their own limitations.

Over one-half of the PWS subjects requested emotional support. This appears to be one of the most neglected areas within rehabilitation. Often this need was not over major or complex situations, but rather a recognition that worries and anxieties were not dealt with in a way that alleviated the individual's concerns. For example, individuals sometimes missed out on family events, or were protected, as in one example, by withholding knowledge of the death of a close relative. In reality, the individual knew that the grandmother had died, but the family decided that it would be better not to include the granddaughter in the funeral arrangements or the family discussions around this sad event. The inability to openly confront this matter in an adult way, and the lack of opportunity to work through the trauma associated with the loss, left the granddaughter in need of emotional support. Allied to the issue of emotional support is the need for friends; help is needed in learning how to make and maintain friendships.

Very often parents are concerned over the temper-tantrums of their PWS children, but the issue is also one for which children have considerable concerns themselves. It is incumbent on rehabilitation practitioners to attempt to work with such needs more directly. The individuals themselves, through skilled behavioural management and counselling by a familiar and respected counsellor, need to be the focal point of the intervention. It is worth noting that parents found behavioural management among the most potent of the assistance provided. It is suggested that this should be taken much further to be personalized by a skilled case-worker within the family environment, as has been done by Brown *et al*. (1988).

Most individuals wanted a greater range of leisure experience, including learning how to organize their own leisure time. This point is recognized by research, and it is apparent that many PWS people have been well aware of this lack in their lives. Help with home management was also seen to be important, and many wanted greater independence. Most wanted help in practical areas, such as budgeting skills. Simple home repairs and concerns over their own temper-tantrums also predominated in the list of areas where help was desired.

The matter of independence is one of the major issues concerning PWS. To allow greater independence requires the development of management systems that move behaviour from external to internal self-control (Brown and Hughson, 1987). Even when this is successful, the internal controls can break down, particularly when the individual is under new or additional stress. This is a part of rehabilitation involving the careful monitoring of behaviour, and the signs of regression need to be noted.

The question of independence for those with PWS is certainly at the centre of quality-of-life concerns. To value choice, and hence permit greater independence, necessarily means permitting greater risk, including risk to health and possibly even life.

Some parents argue that the choice for independence, once self-declared, is essential for optimal quality of life as perceived by the child. Others value health and longevity as more important quality-of-life factors, and seek to structure a more supervised lifestyle. Implicit in such parental decision-making are issues around the parents' own quality of life, with which they must also wrestle.

Value was placed by individuals on personal belongings and a private living area. This relates to impact of ownership on the development of self-image. Somebody said, 'I have my very own telephone', another noted the need for 'one's own place'.

The need to make choices and decisions over what one wants is extremely important, but because of the necessary physical controls examples of possible choice sometimes go unnoticed. One person who did have choices stated he felt good, 'because I can go to places on my own like swimming and the movie theatre', while another noted, 'independence is peaceful'. In this latter instance the language itself expresses ability, but it also notes a common theme, namely independence, respect for privacy, and quietness come high on PWS children's list of needs.

Some females with PWS have male friends, and their level of sexual interest varies considerably. This was also true of PWS males. Ability and experience levels were also widely different. Some of the people we interviewed were concerned with physical abuse, while others were concerned with health issues, particularly 'being fatigued much of the time'. This last concern is also expressed by many handicapped people, and relates to some of the issues of feeling unwell, and, possibly related, not being able, or not having the energy, to carry out activities. It may also be associated with an early ageing process, for most handicapped people do not have the longevity of the non-handicapped population. The issues of ageing need to be addressed more effectively and earlier.

Having made statements about behaviour and variability, it is important to stress that idiosyncracy of choice, expression and ability were very noticeable. Such variability is seen, for example, in where people desire to live. There is often recognition, gratitude, and love expressed for parents, yet the desire for independence is often overriding, particularly among older persons with PWS. Resentment due to lack of privacy was recorded: 'people examine certain belongings that makes me feel very uncomfortable'. Another individual noted, 'I have no key to my room', and perhaps the most impressive, one individual wrote at the end of the questionnaire, 'I AM A SINGLE ADULT', thus emphatically expressing his self-concept as an independent adult.

## SOME GENERAL RECOMMENDATIONS

In the study of quality of life, Brown *et al*. (1989) made 104 recommendations. Most of these are relevant to rehabilitation settings and people with PWS. A few have been singled out for particular mention:

- There are some general physiological and social phenomena that relate to all persons with disabilities. Idiosyncrasy is a central function, and variability needs to be recognized. It is extremely important to listen to the individual's perceptions. Formal as well as informal questioning and discussion are recommended.
- It is important that agencies provide clear and written details of their philosophy, and express these in terms of specific goals. What is done at an agency, what choices are possible, where training takes place, and the expected outcomes are important issues on which parents and the client need to be clear. For example, a sheltered environment may have some protective aspects welcomed by parents. A stimulating community environment with opportunities for choice with appropriate structure may have particular merit for the client. The same concerns apply in regard to education programmes and the involvement with clinics or remedial centres.
- It seems important to change the goals of rehabilitation for adults away from vocational areas to much more concentration on social development, home living, and leisure-time activities. The last needs particular recognition.
- There should be opportunities to deal with worries and anxieties. Skilled counselling should be employed if necessary.

- The relevance of practical home and community-school training, and the need to provide this within the home and local social environment must be recognized. This has many implications for the education of rehabilitation practitioners.
- From an administrative point of view, form-filling should be minimized. Further, it should be recognized by government departments that with the possible advent of individualized funding and contracting of services, there is a need to be much more flexible. Mechanisms should be provided that ensure individuals are not limited in terms of the services they receive.
- Intelligence does not forecast the type of psychological or social treatment an individual may need. To limit treatment to a standard and restricted format because of low intelligence is to relegate many individuals to a life of dependence and care, even though this may be under the guise of attending a rehabilitation agency.
- Staff sensitivity to individual needs is required. Respect for privacy is particularly critical in relation to home living. Most importantly, the individual should be consulted. There are a few guidelines which appear to be of some general use: privacy of space and time; personal care of belongings, which are free from examination by staff or parents; the need for a key to one's flat or room; the need for quiet time; the value of a sense of humour from those who are involved. All of these are high on the list of attributes noted by clients.
- Many of the professional skills involved need to be taught within colleges and universities. They tend not to be learned by attending traditional agencies for disabled persons, but by giving rehabilitation students an opportunity to work in home environments of people with disabilities. Many parents support this and welcome opportunities to involve students and counsellors into the home environment. Others feel their home is a place of privacy, and will not allow access by rehabilitation workers.

Our view is that many of the issues of rehabilitation cannot be dealt with unless the environment in which the person lives becomes part of the rehabilitation process on a daily basis, or at least for several hours each week. This has been recognized in studies from infancy through to adulthood (Mitchell and Brown, 1990).

- It is important for personnel to gain new insights into their own personality styles. Many people believe they give choices or do not oppress clients. The records from clients, however, suggest that psychological oppression is a common feature of many rehabilitation personnel.
- Families need support as early as possible, regardless of whether a diagnosis of PWS has been made.
- The needs of particular clients must be recognized along with those of the family. This relates to better selection of caseworkers or managers and staff, and also to the selection of students for rehabilitation education or special-education programmes.

  Many people choose to work with people with handicaps because of their previous contacts. It does not necessarily follow that they have the right personality characteristics to deal with the dynamic rehabilitation of disabled persons, particularly where this involves following a quality-of-life model. A desire to care for people frequently goes with a practice of controlling what individuals do rather than addressing, promoting, and developing self-image and client self-control.
- It is important to recognize that rehabilitation practitioners and other professionals cannot understand a child unless they have a detailed knowledge of the family. This is important within the education domain as much as in any clinical preserve. The family must be understood in terms of its skills, strengths, and weaknesses, both collectively and as individuals.
- Most parents will provide support, help, care, love, and devotion beyond anything a reliable worker will provide, but a good rehabilitation worker has skills and a knowledge of how to build and apply procedures which may be critical in rehabilitation. In our experience, many professionals working in individual living situations suffer themselves from stress and burn-out once they come to deal with problems facing parents on a day-to-day basis. It is incumbent on rehabilitation services to ensure that stress management is provided on an as-needed basis.

If rehabilitation fails in part or whole, parents have no option but to provide an environment for later life, which will be one of dependence. For this reason, many parents understandably look towards traditional residential options, or long-term residential care within a modern framework. It is important to ensure that this as far as possible is unnecessary, recognizing that it can be prevented by skilled rehabilitation personnel who use individualized intervention. If residential or vocational restriction occurs, then it should be minimized so that individuals have a reasonable opportunity for self-expression, and, hopefully, the type of stimulation which leads to the development of positive self-image within a quality of life which they have personally defined.

## SUMMARY

In addition to a discussion of the conceptual bases of quality-of-life research, this chapter has presented a discussion of quality-of-life issues from the perspective of PWS clients, making comparisons with a broader population of persons with mental handicaps. It is concluded that:

- People with PWS vary greatly in terms of their personal characteristics, and personal and family expectations concerning quality of life. Idiosyncracy of choice and expression are very evident.
- Some PWS clients find attendance at a rehabilitation agency personally restrictive, resulting in unhappiness. They anticipate little change in skill acquisition.
- As a group, people with PWS expressed needs related to:
  - more emotional support;
  - help in practical areas such as budgeting, home repairs, home management;
  - assistance with temper control;
  - desire for a greater range of leisure experience;
  - desire for greater independence;
  - acknowledged ownership of personal belongings;
  - provision of private living space;
  - personal safety and health issues.

- Independence is an important issue between parents and PWS dependants. The desire for independence is a natural correlate of the transition to adult status in our society. To allow greater independence, however, is to seemingly increase the risk to health and life. This is the major dilemma facing PWS parents.
- Quality-of-life considerations require that parents wrestle with philosophical issues such as, the provision of greater protection versus the potential for social and psychological limitation; the parent responsibility to care versus the child's right to make choices; the moral responsibility to protect life versus the individual right to risk life; the opportunity for normalized, integrated experiences versus the provision of homogeneous, segregated experiences; the quality of the PWS child's life versus the quality of life for the parents and siblings.

  These are complex, value-laden dichotomies for which there are few simple answers. Parents need to be well informed with respect to legal rights, and need the support of family and friends as they explore such issues.
- The quality of life of individuals with PWS will be affected by the calibre of the rehabilitation professionals providing support. As much of the work to be done must occur in the home and community environments, practitioners must be skilled, flexible individuals with appropriate personality traits.

*Chapter 10*

# Conclusion

From the medical perspective we have inherited a pathological view of PWS – a syndrome complete with a check-list of characteristics and a label that often has influenced perceptions and services in particular ways. This text, on the other hand, has looked at PWS from a psycho-socio-educational perspective. It emphasizes variations within the syndrome, the normalcy of many behaviours, and the idiosyncracy of choices that are made by those with the condition. It presents a more optimistic view than has been seen to date.

Through collaboration resulting in improvements in early identification, dietary management and weight-control, educational and therapeutic interventions, and community integration, greater longevity and improved quality of life are emerging. Indeed, the fact that researchers are recognizing the need for attention to such topics as community-based residential options, quality of life, and the ageing process should be an encouragement to parents and professionals alike.

The time gap between research results and application of the results to practice is being reduced through parent workshops and less academic communication networks. Service delivery is also improving. Despite the individual criticisms, there is a definite overall improvement being made in the professional recognition of PWS and the accommodation for services. This is not to suggest that the pinnacle has been achieved; to the contrary, much advocacy is still needed. Parents who have felt so isolated in the past are now banding together in mutual-support groups, and while they may be relatively small they are not powerless. Communication has improved from the local to the international level, making information and resources readily available. In some jurisdictions services are beginning to emerge based on individual descriptions rather than on labels, and funding is being individualized. The concept of individualized service dollars is empowering persons with PWS and their families to purchase the services they deem appropriate to their particular needs.

While some parents at this point will feel positive, others may still be frustrated. The foregoing is based on generalizations and meant to be an encouragement. It does not deny the pain associated with each situation. Problems imposed by a rural location, bureaucratic barriers, or a dual diagnosis, for example, can seem overwhelming to those carrying the care-giving responsibility. The stress associated with the intensity of daily-management demands and the prolonged burden of caring can be personally debilitating and disruptive to the family unit. Care must be taken by parents and professionals, however, not to stereotype individuals with PWS or their families. Each person and family circumstance is unique; a syndrome is a range of symptoms, and not every person with PWS will display all characteristics.

The heterogeneity within PWS is often overlooked. As people are classified and labelled, the emphasis is placed on similarities rather than on individual differences. While it may be easy, and valid, to generalize about quantifiable physical characteristics such as height and weight, it is more difficult, and less valid, to make assumptions about dimensions such as personality and behaviour. Further, as with everyone, people with PWS have their hopes and ambitions. It is not uncommon for PWS teenagers, for example, to talk of marrying, living independently, or working at a trendy job. They need assistance to understand the realities of the world they live in and the facts associated with their condition.

The facts at this point in time are relatively few, although there are hypotheses, impressions, and generalizations which may seem to have the authority of fact. Discernment is needed in interpreting what is written on the syndrome, both here and elsewhere. Readers are encouraged to try what seems reasonable for their circumstance, but to be wary of what feels uncomfortable. Just as there is a range of characteristics within the syndrome, there is a variety of potential interventions. The concept of individual differences must therefore be applied to both individual and family situations.

In an encouraging plenary address to the eleventh annual Prader–Willi Syndrome Association conference in Calgary, Neufeldt (1989) presented the preconditions which need to be in place in order to be able to celebrate the differences found in those with PWS. Included were the needs to create inclusive communities, to discern unique gifts, to foster mutual aid and support, and to set time aside to celebrate. He concluded by saying that when these preconditions are spontaneously met, then the presence of a syndrome fades into meaninglessness. It is our hope that this text will contribute to more inclusiveness through increased understanding and better management for those with PWS.

# *Appendix A*

# Glossary of terms

The following terms used in this book are drawn largely from medical literature, and are defined here for the convenience of lay readers.

| | |
|---|---|
| **amyotonia** | Lack of muscle tone. |
| **apraxia** | Difficulty (in this case, with speech) due to a brain lesion. |
| **autosomal recessive inheritance** | A genetic mechanism related to the autosomes. Both parents (usually asymptomatic) must carry the gene concerned to produce an affected child, which occurs when the child inherits that gene from each parent. The risk of recurrence is 25%. |
| **axillary** | The area of the armpit. |
| **asymptomatic** | Without symptoms. |
| **caseness** | A rule defining the level of severity needed for intervention. |
| **cerebral** | Pertaining to the cerebrum, the largest and uppermost part of the brain. |
| **chromosomal banding** | Staining of chromosomes to show a characteristic series of dark and light bands. Each chromosome has a distinct banding pattern. |
| **chromosome** | There are normally 46 chromosomes in each cell of the body responsible for inheritance. These chromosomes have been given numbers. In Prader–Willi it is Chromosome 15 which is recognized as abnormal in 50–70% of cases. |

| | |
|---|---|
| **chronological age** | Actual age in years, months, days, as opposed to mental age, i.e. the level of understanding at which one functions. |
| **clinical diagnosis** | Diagnosis based on direct observation of a patient's characteristics. |
| **95% confidence limits** | The range or interval in which we are 95% certain that the true value lies. |
| **consanguinity** | Blood relationship. |
| **cryptorchidism** | Condition where testes do not descend into the scrotum. |
| **cytogenetic examination** | Laboratory examination of a person's chromosomes by using special techniques. |
| **deletion** | The loss of part of a chromosome. |
| **DNA** | Deoxyribonucleic acid. A fundamental component of living tissue containing the genetic code. |
| **encopresis** | Withholding of bowel movements. |
| **endocrinology** | The study of the endocrine or ductless glands and their internal secretions. |
| **epidemiology** | Distribution of disease within a population; concerned with characteristics such as incidence, prevalence, ethnic, and gender distribution. |
| **extra satellite chromosome** | An additional small chromosome. |
| **gametogenesis** | The process of cell division and differentiation by which mature eggs or sperm develop. |
| **genotype** | The inherent endowment of the individual. |
| **heterogeneous** | Unlike origins. |
| **histologic** | Having to do with microscopic study of tissues. |
| **hyperphagia** | Over-eating. |
| **hypogonadism** | Lack of sexual development. |
| **hypogonadotrophinism** | Low levels of gonad-stimulating hormones. |

| | |
|---|---|
| **hypomentia** | Lack of mental ability. |
| **hypothalamus** | Part of the midbrain, close to the pituitary. |
| **hypotonia** | Lack of muscle tone, tension, strength. |
| **incidence** | Rate of occurrence, i.e. number of births. |
| **karyotype** | The general appearance of the chromosomal makeup of a cell, including the number, size and shape of the chromosomes. |
| **metabolic** | Having to do with biochemical processes in the body. |
| **n** | Sample size. |
| **neonatal** | The first month of a baby's life. |
| **neuro-endocrine** | Pertaining to the nervous system and the endocrine system (i.e., the ductless glands and their internal secretions). |
| **oligophrenia** | Mental deficiency. |
| **organic** | Pertaining to an organ. |
| **paternal or maternal origin** | Originating from the father or mother, respectively. |
| **pathology** | The science which deals with abnormal disease processes and occurrences. |
| **PKU (phenylketonuria)** | Autosomal recessive disease resulting in mental subnormality if not treated with dietary restriction of phenylalanine. |
| **pondostatural index (PSI)** | Weight in pounds divided by height in inches. |
| **prenatal** | Before birth. |
| **prevalence** | Frequency within a population. |
| **proximal** | Nearest to the head or source. |
| **pubic** | In the area of the pubic bone, the centre bone of the front of the pelvis. |

**quartiles** The division of a distribution of individuals in a series into four groups of equal frequency.

**quinquennium** A period of five years.

**stanine** A method of collapsing test scores into groups (stanines) so that they approximate a normal (expected) distribution. These groups are given numbers 1–9. The mean of the stanine scale is 5, and the standard deviation is 1.96. The percentage of cases in the stanine-score categories from 1 to 9 are 4, 7, 12, 17, 20, 17, 12, 7, and 4.

**strabismus** A disorder of the muscles of the eyes in which both eyes cannot be focused on the same point at the same time, resulting in squinting.

**translocation** Relocation of material within a chromosome.

*Appendix B*

# Interventions surveyed

*Medical*

- Regular medical monitoring (GP)
- Regular medical monitoring (specialist)
- Medication
- Hormone treatment
- Hospitalization
- Surgery: eyes; undescended testes; obesity

*Dietary*

- American Dietetic Food Exchange System
- Special diet (e.g. high protein)
- Calorie counting
- Weight-control clinic monitoring
- Self-help weight control group (e.g. Weight-Watchers)
- Nutritionist/dietitian consultation
- Food-preparation training (i.e. menu-planning, cooking)
- Relaxation exercises before meals (e.g. deep-breathing, imagery)

*Allied health*

- Orthodontics
- Chiropractic
- Ophthalmology
- Psychotherapy: group; individual

*Environmental*

- Locks on food cupboards; kitchen entry door(s)
- Restricted activities in the kitchen
- Counters always cleared
- No food preparation privileges
- No food allowed in other rooms
- Supervision while shopping
- Controls on spending money

*Behavioural*

Deprivation of food
Deprivation of privileges
Physical punishment
Isolation or confinement
Praise
Token or point system
Use of non-food reinforcers
Practice role playing
Early preparation for coming events

*Developmental*

Infant stimulation programme
Handicap swim programme
Home exercise programme
Speech/language therapy
Art therapy/training
Music therapy/training
Special-education classes
Fitness classes
Work experience/on-the-job training

*Social*

PWS peer friendships facilitated
Integrated (regular) youth group participation
Summer camp programme (special/handicap; integrated)
Socialization programme (i.e. personal child-care worker/activity-aide time assigned to aid socialization)
Sunday school/church/or other religious involvement
Social worker assigned
Competitive sports (e.g. Special Olympics)

*Parental*

PWS parent group association participation
Respite care (i.e. agency supplied parent-relief time)
Family baby-sitting support
Co-operative baby-sitting with other PWS families
Private baby-sitting
Counselling: stress; marital
Family therapy

*Source*: James (1987).

## *Appendix C*

# Professionals working with PWS

| | |
|---|---|
| **broker** | Assists with the identification of supports necessary for independent living, securing the funding resources and negotiating customized services with government agencies and private agencies and independent service providers. |
| **child neurologist** | Medical doctor diagnosing and providing treatment for problems of the nervous system. |
| **chiropractor** | Treats disease based on the theory that disease is caused by interference with nerve function and employing manipulation of the body joints, especially of the spine, in seeking to restore normal nerve function. |
| **community living skills worker** | Supplies supports to individuals with handicaps living independently or semi-independently in the community. |
| **counsellor** | Provides advice, assistance in clarifying values, setting goals, dealing with personal problems; school counsellors particularly knowledgeable about educational areas; qualifications of community-based counsellors vary greatly. |
| **dietitian** | A specialist in diets. |
| **endocrinologist** | A medical doctor specializing in working with the endocrine glands and the internal secretions of the body. |

| | |
|---|---|
| **early childhood education specialist** | Provides educational programmes at the nursery-school level. |
| **GP (General practitioner)** | Medical doctor providing ongoing general health treatment; refers to other medical specialists when necessary. |
| **geneticist** | Identifies those conditions which are inherited and which could recur in other children in the family; conducts chromosome analysis. |
| **infant development worker** | Provides advice on infant stimulation programmes, nutritional advice, developmental-growth expectations. |
| **neonatologist** | Medical doctor providing special health care to newborn babies. |
| **nutritionist** | A specialist in nutrition. |
| **occupational therapist** | Provides assistance with self-help skills such as dressing and eating by using exercises, toys and assistive devices. |
| **ophthalmologist** | Medical doctor dealing with the structure, functions and diseases of the eye. |
| **orthodontist** | Dentist concerned with correcting and preventing irregularities of the teeth, and poor occlusion. |
| **paediatrician** | Medical doctor providing general health care for children. |
| **paediatric nurse** | Nurse specializing in care of children. |
| **physiatrist** | Provides physical therapy assistance for those with neuromuscular handicaps. |
| **physiotherapist** | Provides information and exercises to help with posture and body movements. |
| **psychiatrist** | A medical doctor specializing in the diagnosis and treatment of mental illness. |

| | |
|---|---|
| **psychologist** | Evaluates and provides suggestions about a child's social, emotional, and educational development. Psychologists specialize in such areas as child development, education, or rehabilitation. |
| **social worker** | Provides access to and information about community services available. Key persons for accessing government social services or those private contracted services funded by government social services departments. May also provide or facilitate individual and family counselling in some areas. |
| **special educator** | Teacher trained in a knowledge of disabilities, remedial instruction, alternative methodologies, curriculum adaptation, individualized programming, etc. They may function as segregated special-educational classroom teachers, learning-assistance teachers, resource-room teachers, or itinerant specialists. |

# *Appendix D*

# PWS organizations

**Australia**
PWA – Australia
c/o Valeria Gow
Box 1028
Burwood N., NSW 2134
Australia

PWSA – Victoria
c/o Don Robertson
14 Prospect Ct.
Ringwood, Victoria 3134
Australia

PWSA – West Australia
c/o Dawn Taylor
173 Waterford Dr.
Hillarys, 6025
West Australia

**Belgium**
Prader–Willi Vereniging
Wilfred Deley, President
Boechoutsesteenweg 54
2540 Hove
Belgium

**Canada**
PWSA of Alberta
c/o Doris Chura
2002 32nd Ave S.W.
Calgary, AB
Canada T2T 1W6

PWSA of Central Canada
c/o Rick Johnson
Box 414
Stonewall, Manitoba
Canada R0C 2Z0

Lower Mainland PWSA
c/o Vodia Parker
2064 Hadfield Ct
Burlington, Ont.
Canada L7P 4S5

Ontario PWSA
c/o Pat Eaton, President
42 Elmbank Cres.
Nepean, Ontario
Canada K2G 3P6

**Denmark**
Landsforeningen – PWS Denmark
c/o Susanne Blichfeldt, MD
Kildehusvej 12
Roskilde 4000
Denmark

**England**
PWSA – United Kingdom
30 Follett Dr.
Abbots Langley, Herts
England WD5 0LP

**France**
Francine Bonasos
13 Traverse du Cardinal
34980 Saint Gely du Sesc
France

**Netherlands**
Prader–Willi Vereniging
HPW Moezelaar
Ziggenstraat 30
Geldrop 5662RM
Netherlands

**Nigeria**
Prof. Amialu Mariam Koroka, Pres.
Chromosome Dept.
PO Box 32, Katcha
Zago, Grako Local Gout
Niger State
Nigeria

**New Zealand**
PWSA (NZ)
c/o Linda Thornton
Co-ordinator/Secretary
c/-8 Mallam St.
Karori, Wellington 5
New Zealand
04-763-179

**Norway**
Christine Bauer
Nils Andreassen
Trosterudveien 2 G
0386 Oslo 3
Norway

**South Africa**
Birgit Schroder Hedsbjerg
PO Box 914
Sloane Park 2152
Johannesburg
South Africa

**Sweden**
Jean Philips Martinnson
Stockrosvagen 10, S 12232
Enskede
Stockholm
Sweden

**United States**
Prader–Willi Syndrome Association
6490 Excelsior Blvd., E-102
St Louis Park, MN 55426
United States of America

*Appendix E*

# Canadian-specific terms

The following terms used in this text may have distinctively Canadian meanings.

| | |
|---|---|
| **boarding home** | A home, other than the parents' home, which provides a room and board (meals) for a single adult. |
| **educable mentally handicapped** | Also known as 'mildly mentally handicapped.' Students with low intellectual abilities which may limit their academic achievement to the upper intermediate grades. They are usually characterized by delayed physical and social development as well. |
| **Education levels** | There is some variation in age range for particular school levels. The following represent common age groupings for children. |

| | |
|---|---|
| Pre-school | less than 5-years of age |
| Kindergarten | 5-years of age |
| Elementary | 5–12-years of age |
| Secondary | 12–18-years of age |
| Post-secondary (tertiary) | 19-years upwards |

Completion of grade 12 is the level required for entry to most tertiary education.

| | |
|---|---|
| **food bank** | Agency responsible for the distribution of food to needy persons. Receives donations from private donors and retail outlets. |
| **individualized service dollars** | Service dollars based on individual needs and allocated to people, not programmes or places. Funding may be dispersed, managed and monitored by a third party through a community autonomous board, or be given directly to the person, family or guardian/trustee and the supports they choose. |
| **infant stimulation** | Early individualized intervention programmes for infants with established risk (e.g. conditions associated with mental retardation, with biological risk (e.g. premature birth) or environmental risk (e.g. lack of adequate stimulation in infancy). Purpose of programming is to provide fullest possible development. Services are offered under a variety of auspices and include centre and home-based services. |
| **interns** | Doctors serving an apprenticeship as an assistant resident in a hospital, generally just after graduation from medical school. |
| **learning disabled** | Students characterized by a processing disorder which affects their understanding of the use of symbols or spoken language, or having a significant discrepancy between their estimated learning potential and actual performance. Not usually attributable to sensory or physical impairment, mental retardation, emotional disturbance, environmental or cultural disadvantage or lack of opportunity to learn. |

**Ministry of Human Resources**
A provincial government ministry responsible for the provision of social services (e.g. income assistance, child protection, services to mentally handicapped persons). Term varies across provinces.

**moderately mentally handicapped**
Formerly known as 'trainable mentally handicapped'. Students have low intellectual ability and generally will not attain academic skills beyond a primary-grade level. The behaviour of these students is generally not appropriate to their chronological age.

**provinces**
Major geographical and political divisions within Canada. Each province has legislative responsibility for areas not managed by the federal government, e.g. education, social services.

# References


Alexander, R.C. and Greenswag, L.R. (1988) Medical and nursing interventions, in *Management of Prader-Willi Syndrome* (eds L.R. Greenswag and R.C. Alexander), Springer-Verlag, NY, pp.55–57.

Alexander, R.C. and Hanson, J.W. (1988) Overview, in *Management of Prader–Willi Syndrome* (eds L.R. Greenswag and R.C. Alexander), Springer-Verlag, NY, pp.3–14.

Angulo, M.A., Castro-Magana, M., Palekar, A. and Sabbath, M. (1989) Deletion of chromosome 15q11.2–12 associated with obesity and learning disorders without clinical features of Prader–Willi syndrome. *Clinical Genetics*, **35**, 304.

Bahling, E. (1979) Prader–Willi syndrome: two case studies. *School Psychology Digest*, **8**(1), 133–6.

Beck-Ford, V. and Brown, R.I. (1984), in collaboration with Gillberry, M. and Rolf, C. *Leisure Training and Rehabilitation: A Programme Manual*, Charles C. Thomas, Springfield, IL.

Beckman, P. (1983) Influence of selected child characteristics on stress in families of handicapped infants. *American J. of Mental Deficiency*, **88**(2), 150–6.

Bernstein, G., Ziarnik, J., Rudrud, E. and Czajkowski, L. (1981) *Behavioral Habilitation Through Proactive Programming*, Paul H. Brookes, Baltimore MD.

Borthwick-Duffy, S.A. (1986) Quality of life of mentally retarded people: a developmental model, unpublished doctoral dissertation. Univ. of California, School of Education, Riverside, CA.

Branson, C. (1981) Speech and language characteristics of children with Prader–Willi syndrome, in *Prader–Willi Syndrome*, (eds V. Holm, S. Sulzbacher and P. Pipes), Univ. Park Press, Baltimore MD. pp.179–83.

Bray, G., Dahms, W., Swerdloff, R., Fiser, R. *et al*. (1983) The Prader–-Willi syndrome: a study of 40 patients and a review of the literature, *Medicine*, **62**(2), 59–80.

Brissenden, J.E. and Levy, E.P. (1973) Prader–Willi syndrome in infant monozygotic twins. *American J. of Diseases of Children*, **126**, 110–12.

Brooks-Bertrum, P. and Mitchell, W. (1986) Support groups and advocacy, parent survival, in *Proceedings of the Prader–Willi Syndrome Association Eighth National Conference*, Prader–Willi Syndrome Association, Edina, MN, pp.115–26.

Brown, R.I. and Bayer, M.B. (1991) Rehabilitation programmes. Quality of life questionnaire. Univ. of Calgary, Rehabilitation Studies, in press.

Brown, R.I., Bayer, M.B. and Brown, P.M. (1988) Quality of life: a challenge for rehabilitation agencies. *Australia & New Zealand J. of Developmental Disabilities*, **14**(3/4), pp.189–99.

Brown, R.I., Bayer, M.B. and Brown, P.M. (1992) *Quality of life. The Impact of Choice on Programmes for Adults with Developmental Handicaps*, in preparation.

Brown, R.I., Bayer, M.B. and MacFarlane, C.M. (1989) *Rehabilitation Programmes: The Performance and Quality of Life of Adults with Developmental Handicaps*, Lugus, Toronto.

Brown, R.I. and Chazan, M. (1989) *Learning Difficulties and Emotional Problems*, Detselig, Calgary.

Brown, R.I. and Hughson, E.A. (1987) *Behavioural and Social Rehabilitation and Training*, John Wiley, London.

Burke, C.M., Kouseff, B.G., Gleeson, M., O'Connell, B.M. *et al*. (1987) Familial Prader–Willi syndrome. *Archives of Internal Medicine*, **147**, 673–5.

Butler, M.G., Meaney, F.J. and Palmer, C.G. (1986) Clinical and cytogenetic survey of 39 individuals with Prader–Labhart–Willi syndrome. *American J. of Medical Genetics*, **23**, 793–809.

Butler, M.G., Weaver, D.D. and Meaney, F.G. (1982) Prader–Willi syndrome: are there population differences? *Clinical Genetics* **22**(5), 292–4.

Byrne, E.A., and Cunningham, C.C. (1987) Lifestyle and satisfaction in families of children with Down's syndrome, in *Rehabilitation Education*, (ed R.I. Brown), Croom Helm, London; Vol.3, pp.83–110.

Caldwell, M.L. and Taylor, R.L. (1986) Description of an innovative intervention program for individuals with Prader–Willi syndrome. *B.C. J. of Special Education*, **10**(2), 183–7.

Carlson, B. (1984) Behavior study update. *The Gathered View*, **10**(3), 8.

Carpenter, S.P. (1989) Development of a young man with Prader–Willi syndrome and secondary functional encopresis. *Canadian J. of Psychiatry*, **34**(2), 123–6.

Cassidy, S.B. (1984) Prader–Willi syndrome. *Current Problems in Pediatrics*, **14**(1).

Cassidy, S.B. (1986) Overview of PWS. Paper presented at the Prader–Willi Syndrome Association Eighth National Conference, June 1986, Sacramento, CA.

Cassidy, S.B., Gainey, A.J. and Butler, M.G. (1989) Paternal hydrocarbon exposure at conception in Prader–Willi syndrome patient with and without deletions of chromosome 15q. *Clinical Genetics*, **35**, 307.

Cassidy, S.B., Thuline, H.C. and Holm, V.A. (1984) Deletion of chromosome 15(q11;q13) in Prader–Labhart–Willi syndrome clinic population. *American J. of Medical Genetics*, **17**, 485–95.

Chamberlin, J. and Magenis, R.E. (1980) Parental origin of de novo chromosome rearrangements. *Human Genetics*, **53**, 343–7.

Charrow, J., Balkin, N. and Cohen, M.M. (1983) Translocations in Prader–Willi syndrome. *Clinical Genetics*, **23**, 304–7.

Clarren, S.K. and Smith, D.W. (1977) Prader–Willi syndrome: Variable severity and recurrence risk. *American J. of Diseases of Children*, **131**(7), 798–800.

Cohen, M.M. and Gorlin, R.J. (1969) The Prader–Willi syndrome. *American J. of Diseases of Children*, **114**, 213–18.

Cohen, M.M., Hall, B.D., Smith, D.W., Graham, C.B. and Lampert, K.J. (1973) A new syndrome with hypotonia, obesity, mental deficiency, and facial, oral, ocular and limb abnormalities. *The J. of Pediatrics*, **83**, 280–5.

Conn-Blowers, E. and McLeod, H. (1989) Special education in Alberta, in *Special Education Across Canada* (eds M. Cscapo and L. Goguen) Centre for Human Development and Research, Vancouver, BC, pp.19–28.

Crnic, K.A., Friedrich, W.N. and Greenberg, M.T. (1983) Adaptation of families with mentally retarded children: A model of stress, coping and family ecology. *American J. of Mental Deficiency*, **88**(2), 125–38.

Crnic, K.A., Sulzbacher, S., Snow, J. and Holm, V.A. (1980) Preventing mental retardation associated with gross obesity in the Prader–Willi syndrome. *Pediatrics*, **66**, 787–9.

Cummings, S.T., Bayley, H.C. and Rie, H.E. (1966) Effects of the child's deficiency on the mother: a study of mothers of mentally retarded, chronically ill and neurotic children. *American J. of Orthopsychiatry*, **36**, 595–608.

Day, H.I. (1988) *Quality of life of people with disabilities*. Keynote address, Quality of life. Fourth Canadian Congress of Rehabilitation, Toronto.

DeFraites, E.B., Thurmon, T.F. and Farhadian, H. (1975) Familial Prader–Willi syndrome. *Birth defects: Original article series*, **11**(4), 123–6.

DeFrance, H.F., Beemer, F.A. and Ippel, P.F. (1984) Duplication in chromosome 15q in a boy with the Prader–Willi syndrome: further cytogenetic confusion. *Clinical Genetics*, **26**, 379–82.

Derogatis, L.R. (1983) *SCL-90-R: Administration, scoring and procedures manual-II*, 2nd edn, Clinical Psychometric Research, Towson, MD.

Doernberg, N.L. (1982) Issues in communication between pediatricians and parents of young mentally retarded children. *Pediatric Annals*, **11**, 438–44.

Drotar, D. (1981) Psychological perspectives in chronic childhood illness. *J. of Pediatric Psychology*, **6**(3), 211–28.

Dunn, H.G., Ford, D.K., Auersperg, N. and Miller, J.R. (1961) Benign congenital hypotonia with chromosomal anomaly. *Pediatrics*, **28**, 578–91.

Dunn, H.G. (1968) The Prader–Labhart–Willi syndrome: review of the literature and report of nine cases. *Acta Paediatrica Scandinavica*, **186**, 1–38.

Dunn, H.G., Tze, W.J., Alisharan, R.M. and Schulzer, M. (1981) Clinical experience with 23 cases of Prader–Willi syndrome, in *Prader–Willi Syndrome* (eds V.A. Holm, S. Sulzbacher and P. Pipes), University Park Press, Baltimore MD, pp.121–35.

Dunn, L.M. and Dunn, L.M. (1981) *Peabody Picture Vocabulary Test – Revised Manual for Forms L and M*. American Guidance Service, Circle Pines, MN.

Education Act (1980) *Revised Statutes of Ontario, c.*129, Queen's Printer, Toronto.

Endo, M., Tasaka, N., Matsuura, N. and Matsuda, I. (1976) Laurence-Moon-Biedl syndrome and Prader–Willi syndrome in a single family. *European J. of Paediatrics*, **123**(4), 269–76.

Evans, P.R. (1969) The Prader–Labhart–Willi syndrome. *Developmental Medicine and Child Neurology*, **11**(13), 380–2.

Fracarro, M., Suffardi, O., Buhler, E.M. and Jurik, L.P. (1977) 15/15 translocation in Prader–Willi syndrome. *J. of Medical Genetics*. **14**(4), 275–6.

Freitag, G., Kingdon, D., Quinn, J. and Shannon, N. (1986) *The outcome of residential treatment with Prader–Willi syndrome children and adolescents: The first four years of the Dubnoff Center Prader–Willi Syndrome Project*. Dubnoff Center for Child Development and Educational Therapy, North Hollywood, CA.

Friedrich, W.N. (1979) Predictors of coping behavior of mothers of handicapped children. *J. of Consulting and Clinical Psychology*, **47**(6), 1140–1.

Friedrich, W.N., Wilturner, L.T. and Cohen, D.S. (1985) Coping resources and parenting mentally retarded children. *American J. of Mental Deficiency*, **90**(2), 130–9.

Gabel, S., Tarter, R.E., Gavaler, J., Golden, W.L., *et al.* (1986) Neuropsychological capacity of Prader–Willi children: general and specific aspects of impairment. *Applied Research in Mental Retardation,* **7**, 459–66.

Gall, R.S. (1984) Special education, in *Dialogue on Disability: A Canadian Perspective* (eds N. Marlett, R. Gall and E. Wight-Felske), Univ. of Calgary Press, Calgary, AB, pp.27–46.

*The Gathered View* (1990a) Telephone study produces results. Prader-Willi Syndrome Association newsletter, **16**(4) (July–August), 1.

*The Gathered View* (1990b) Medical alert: Prader–Willi Syndrome. Prader–Willi Syndrome Association newsletter, **16**(4) (July–August), 5.

Goguen, L. (1989) Evolving educational rights of exceptional children in Canada, in *Special Education Across Canada* (eds M. Csapo and L. Goguen), Centre for Human Development and Research, Vancouver, BC. pp.159–66.

Goh, K., Hermann, M.A., Campbell, R.G. and Thompson, D. (1984) Abnormal chromosome in Prader–Willi syndrome. *Clinical Genetics,* **26**, 597–601.

Goldenberg, S.M. (1990) The evaluation of client choice as perceived by rehabilitation staff in two countries. Unpublished MSc thesis, Univ. of Calgary.

Goldman, J.J. (1983) Group counseling with Prader–Willi clients, *The Gathered View,* **10**(4), 7–8.

Goldman, J.J. (1988) Prader–Willi syndrome in two institutionalized older adults. *Mental Retardation,* **26**(2), 97–102.

Goode, D.A. (1988) *Discussing quality of life: The process and findings of the work group on quality of life for persons with disabilities,* Mental Retardation Institute, New York Medical College, NY.

Gordon, P. and Clarke-Bruyn, R. (1991) Prader–Willi syndrome: the potential of behavior analysis in building healthier lifestyles. *J. of Practical Approaches to Developmental Handicap,* **15**(1), 8–12.

Government of British Columbia (1989) Minister's order no. 13, Ministry of Education, Victoria.

Government of Canada (1981) 1981 census of Canada (Catalog 99–933), Statistics Canada, Ottawa.

Government of Canada (1984) The Charter of Rights and Freedoms: A Guide for Canadians, Publications Canada, Ottawa.

Government of Canada (1985a) Births and deaths (Catalog 84–204), Statistics Canada, Ottawa.

Government of Canada (1985b) Population estimates (Catalog 91–210), Statistics Canada, Ottawa.

Greenswag, L.R. (1984a) The adult with Prader–Willi syndrome: a descriptive investigation. Unpub. doctoral dissertation, Univ. of Iowa, Univ. Microfilms International No. 8423561.

Greenswag, L.R. (1984b) The child with Prader–Willi syndrome grows up. Paper presented at the First Canadian Conference on Prader–Willi Syndrome, October, 1984, McMaster Univ., Hamilton, Ontario, Canada.

Greenswag, L.R. (1988) Understanding psychosexuality, in *Management of Prader–Willi syndrome* (eds L.R. Greenswag and R.C. Alexander), Springer-Verlag, NY, pp.171–81.

Greenswag, L. and Alexander, R. (1988) *Management of Prader–Willi syndrome*, Springer-Verlag, NY.

Gregory, C., Schwart, J. and Hamerton, J.L. (1989) RFLP analysis of eight new Prader–Willi syndrome (PWS) families and 18 new individual patients has revealed chromosome deletions in karyotypically normal patients and the parental origin of the aberrant chromosome is consistently paternal. *American J. of Human Genetics*, **45**(4), A191 Abstract.

Griffiths, D., Quinsey, V. and Hingsburger, D. (1989) *Changing Inappropriate Sexual Behavior: A Community-Based Approach for Persons with Developmental Disabilities*. Paul H. Brookes, Toronto.

Guanti, G. (1980) A new case of rearrangement of chromosome 15 associated with Prader–Willi syndrome. *Clinical Genetics*, **17**, 423–7.

Gunzburg, H.C. (1968) *Social Competence and Mental Handicap*, Bailliere, Tindall & Cassell, London.

Gunzburg, H.C. (1977) *Progress Assessment Chart of social and personal development, manual*, 5th edn, SEFA Publications, Stratford-on-Avon, England.

Gunzburg, H.C. (1983) *PAC Bulletin 1983–1984*, SEFA Publications, Stratford-on-Avon, England.

Hall, B.D. and Smith, D.W. (1972) Prader–Willi syndrome: a resume of 32 cases including an instance of affected first cousins, one of whom is of normal stature and intelligence. *J. of Pediatrics*, **81**, 286–93.

Hanson, J.W. (1981) A view of the etiology and pathogenesis of Prader–Willi syndrome, in *Prader–Willi Syndrome* (eds. V. A. Holm, S. J. Sulzbacher, and P. Pipes), Univ. Park Press, Baltimore, pp.45–53.

Hawkey, C.J. and Smithies, A. (1976) The Prader–Willi syndrome with a 15/15 translocation: Case report and review of the literature. *J. of Medical Genetics*, **13**, 152–7.

Heinemann, A. and Tomaseski-Heinemann, J. (1983) Behaviour and weight management (0–13 years). Paper presented at Prader–Willi Syndrome Association Fifth Annual National Conference, June 1983, San Diego, CA.

Hermann, J. (1981) Implications of Prader–Willi syndrome for the individual and family, in *Prader–Willi Syndrome,* (eds V.A. Holm, S.J. Sulzbacher and P. Pipes), Univ. Park Press, Baltimore, pp.229–44.

Hoefnagel, D., Costello, P.J. and Hatoum, K. (1967) Prader–Willi syndrome. *J. of Mental Deficiency Research,* **11**, 1–11.

Holm, V.A. (1981a) The diagnosis of Prader–Willi syndrome, in *Prader–Willi Syndrome* (eds V.A. Holm, S.J. Sulzbacher, and P. Pipes), Univ. Park Press, Baltimore, pp.37–44.

Holm, V.A. (1981b) Medical management of Prader–Willi syndrome, in *Prader–Willi Syndrome* (eds V.A. Holm, S. J. Sulzbacher, and P. Pipes), Univ. Park Press, Baltimore, pp.261–7.

Holm, V.A. and Pipes, P.L. (1976) Food and children with Prader–Willi syndrome. *American J. of Diseases of Children,* **130**, 1063.

Holroyd, J. and Guthrie, D. (1979) Stress in families of children with neuromuscular disease. *J. of Clinical Psychology,* **35**(4), 734–9.

Holroyd, J. and McArthur, D. (1976) Mental retardation and stress on the parents: a contrast between Down's syndrome and childhood autism. *American J. of Mental Deficiency,* **80**(4), 431–6.

Hornby, G. (in press) Counselling family members of people with disabilities, in *Rehabilitation counselling* (eds. S. Robertson and R.I. Brown), Chapman & Hall, London.

Ikeda, K., Asaka, A., Inouye, E., Kaihara, H. *et al.* (1973) Monozygotic twins concordant for Prader–Willi syndrome. *Japanese J. of Human Genetics,* **18**(2), 220–5.

James, T.N. (1985) The Prader–Willi syndrome adolescent in an educational setting. *J. of Practical Approaches to Developmental Handicap,* **9**(2), 13–17.

James, T.N. (1987) Social and psychological aspects of Prader–Willi syndrome. Unpub. doctoral dissertation, Univ. of Calgary, Alberta.

James, T.N. (1989a) Home intervention and stress control in transcript of 1989 11th Annual National PWSA Conference, Calgary, Alberta, pp.7–15.

James, T.N. (1989b) Prader–Willi syndrome. *Bulletin of the Hereditary Diseases Program of Alberta,* **8**(3), 9–12.

James, T.N. (1991) Prader–Willi syndrome: Home and community intervention strategies. *J. of Practical Approaches to Developmental Handicap,* **15**(1), 13–21.

James, T.N. and Willott, G. (1989) *Prader–Willi syndrome: residential options in western Canada.* The Prader–Willi Syndrome Association of Alberta, Calgary.

Janalee (1982) *Sometimes I'm mad, sometimes I'm glad.* Prader–Willi Syndrome Association, Edina, MN.

Jancar, J. (1971) Prader–Willi syndrome. *J. of Mental Deficiency Research,* **15**, 20–9.

King, G. (1988) Help wanted: Relief for parents. *Entourage*, **3**(2), 26–32.

Kornblatt, E.S. and Heinrich, J. (1985) Needs and coping abilities in families of children with developmental disabilities. *Mental Retardation*, **23**(1), 13–19.

Kousseff, B.G. (1980) Chromosome abnormality in Prader–Willi syndrome. *Clinical Genetics*, **17**, 364–6.

Laurance, B.M., Brito, A. and Wilkinson, J. (1981) Prader–Willi syndrome after age 15 years. *Archives of Disease in Childhood*, **56**, 181–6.

Laurnen, E.L. (1981) Scoliosis in Prader–Willi syndrome, in *Prader–Willi Syndrome* (eds V.A. Holm, S. J. Sulzbacher, and P. Pipes), Univ. Park Press, Baltimore, pp.293–8.

Leconte, J.M. (1981) Social work intervention strategies for families with children with Prader–Willi syndrome, in *Prader–Willi Syndrome* (eds V.A. Holm, S.J. Sulzbacher, and P. Pipes), Univ. Park Press, Baltimore, pp. 245–57.

Ledbetter, D., Riccardi, V., Airhart, S., Strobel, R. *et al*. (1981) Deletions of chromosome 15 as a cause of the Prader–Willi syndrome. *New England J. of Medicine*, **304**, 325–9.

Lubinsky, M., Zellweger, H., Greenswag, L., Larson, G. *et al*. (1987) Familial Prader–Willi syndrome with normal chromosomes. *American J. of Medical Genetics*, **28**, 37–43.

Lupi, M.H. (1988) Education of the child with Prader–Willi syndrome in *Management of Prader–Willi Syndrome* (eds L.R. Greenswag and R.C. Alexander), Springer-Verlag, NY, pp.112–23.

Mackay, A.W. (1984) *Education Law in Canada*, Emond-Montgomery.

Marlett, N.J. (ed.) (1988) *Independent service brokerage*, The Walter Dinsdale Center, Calgary.

Marlett, N.J. (1991) Voices of young adults who live with Prader–Willi syndrome. *J. of Practical Approaches to Developmental Handicap*, **15**(1), 22–25.

Marshall, B.D., Wallace, C.J., Elder, J., Burke, K. *et al*. (1981) A behavioural approach to treatment of Prader–Willi syndrome, in *Prader–Willi Syndrome* (eds V.A. Holm, S. J. Sulzbacher, and P. Pipes), Univ. Park Press, Baltimore, pp.185–99.

Masheim, P. (1981) Psychological data and course in psychotherapy of three mildly retarded adolescents with the Prader–Willi syndrome. *Child Psychiatry Quarterly*, **14**(3), 59–63.

Mattei, J.F., Mattei, M.G. and Giraud, F. (1983) Prader–Willi syndrome and chromosome 15. *Human Genetics*, **64**, 356–62.

Mitchell, L. (1988) *An overview of the Prader–Willi syndrome*. Prader–Willi Syndrome Association, Edina, MN.

Mitchell, W. (1988). Social skills training, in *Management of Prader–Willi*

*Syndrome,* (eds L.R. Greenswag and R.C. Alexander), Springer-Verlag, NY, pp.165–70.

Mitchell, D. and Brown, R.I. (eds) (1990) *Rehabilitation Education Series Volume 4,* Chapman & Hall, London.

Munson-Davis, J.A. (1988) Speech and language development, in *Management of Prader–Willi syndrome,* (eds L.R. Greenswag and R.C. Alexander), Springer-Verlag, NY, pp.124–33.

Nardella, M.T., Sulzbacher, S.J. and Worthington-Roberts, B.S. (1983) Activity levels of persons with Prader–Willi syndrome. *American J. of Mental Deficiency,* **87**(5), 498–505.

Nash, J.B. (1953) *Philosophy of recreation and leisure,* William C. Brown, Dubuque, IA.

Neason, S.A. (1978) *Prader–Willi syndrome: A Handbook for Parents,* Prader–Willi Syndrome Association, Edina, MN.

Nielsen, S.L. and Sulzbacher, S. (1981) Relaxation training with youngsters with Prader–Willi syndrome, in *Prader–Willi Syndrome* (eds V.A. Holm, S. J. Sulzbacher, and P. Pipes), Univ. Park Press, Baltimore, pp.219–27.

Nowak, A.J. (1988) Dental manifestations and management, in *Management of Prader–Willi syndrome,* (eds L. Greenswag and R. Alexander), Springer-Verlag, NY, pp.71–5.

Neufeldt, A. (1989) Celebrating Differences, in transcript of 1989 11th Annual National PWSA Conference, Alberta, Canada, pp.1–6.

Nugent, J.K. and Holm, V.A. (1981) Physical growth in Prader–Willi syndrome, in *Prader–Willi Syndrome* (eds V.A. Holm, S. J. Sulzbacher, and P. Pipes), Univ. Park Press, Baltimore, pp.269–80.

Page, T., Finney, J., Parrish, J. and Iwata, B. (1983a) Assessment and reduction of food stealing in Prader–Willi children. *Applied Research in Mental Retardation,* **4**, 219–28.

Page, T.J., Stanley, A.E., Richman, G.S., Deal, R.M. *et al.* (1983b) Reduction of food theft and long-term maintenance of weight loss in a Prader–Willi adult. *J. of Behaviour Therapy and Experimental Psychiatry,* **14**(3), 261–8.

Parmenter, T.R. (1988) An analysis of the dimensions of quality of life for people with physical disabilities, in *Quality of Life for Handicapped People* (ed. R.I. Brown), Croom Helm, NY, pp.7–36.

Pipes, P. (1981) Weight control, in *Prader–Willi syndrome: A Handbook for Parents* (ed. S.A. Neason), Prader–Willi Syndrome Association, Edina, MN, pp.12–17.

Prader, A., Labhart, A. and Willi, H. (1956) A syndrome of obesity, short stature, cryptorchidism, and oligophrenia, with amyotonia in the newborn period. *Schweizersche Medizinische Wochenschrift,* **86**, 1260–1.

Prader–Willi California Association (1988). Information distributed at the tenth annual National Prader–Willi Syndrome Conference, June 1988, Louisville, KY.

Prader–Willi Syndrome Association (1984) *Synopsis, Prader–Willi syndrome and association*. Edina, MN.

Prader–Willi Syndrome Association (nd) *What educators should know about Prader–Willi syndrome*. St Louis Park, MN.

Province of Alberta (1984) *Vital statistics annual review, 1984*. Social Services and Community Health, Vital Statistics, Edmonton.

Province of Alberta (1988) *Bill 27. The School Act*. Queen's Printer, Edmonton.

Sechrist, A.N. (1986) Diet and nutrition, in *Proceedings of the Prader–Willi Syndrome Association Eighth National Conference*, Prader–Willi Syndrome Association, Edina, MN, pp.18–27.

Schalock, R.L. (1988) The concept of quality of life in community-based mental retardation programs, in *Issues in special education and rehabilitation*, (ed S. Reiter), Omnah Association for Developmentally Disabled People.

Shipe, D. (1984) Early intervention, in *Dialogue on disability: A Canadian Perspective* (eds N. Marlett, R. Gall, and A. Wight-Felske), The Univ. of Calgary Press, Calgary, Vol. 1, pp.15–25.

Sobsey, D. (1988) Sexual offenses and disabled victims: Research and practical implications. *Vis-a-vis: A national newsletter on family violence*, **6**(4), 1–2.

Statistics Canada (1990) Life tables, Canada and provinces, 1985–87 (Catalogue 82-003), in *The Health Reports*, Suppl. 13, Vol. 2 (4), Canadian Centre for Health Information, Statistics Canada, Ottawa.

Steffes, M., Holm, V. and Sulzbacher, S. (1981) The Prader–Willi syndrome: historical perspective, in *The Prader–Willi Syndrome* (eds V. A. Holm, S. J. Sulzbacher and P. Pipes), Univ. Park Press, Baltimore, pp.1–15.

Stephenson, J.B. (1980) Prader–Willi syndrome: Neonatal presentation and later development. *Developmental Medicine and Child Neurology*, **22**, 792–9.

Sulzbacher, S., Crnic, K.A. and Snow, J. (1981) Behavioral and cognitive disabilities in Prader–Willi syndrome, in *Prader–Willi Syndrome* (eds V.A. Holm, S. J. Sulzbacher, and P. Pipes), Univ. Park Press, Baltimore, pp.147–59.

Thompson, D. (1986) Behavioral management programs. Paper presented at the meeting of the Eighth Annual Prader–Willi Syndrome Association Conference, June 1986, Sacramento, CA.

Thompson, D.G, Greenswag, L.R. and Eleazer, R. (1988) Residential programs for individuals with Prader–Willi syndrome, in *Management of Prader–Willi Syndrome* (eds. L.R. Greenswag and R.C. Alexander), Springer-Verlag, NY, pp.205–22.

Thuline, H.C. (1987) Further notes on the etiology of Down's syndrome, in *New Perspectives on Down's Syndrome* (eds. S.M. Pueschel, C. Tingey, J.E. Rynders, A.C. Crocker and D. M. Crutcher), Paul H. Brookes, Baltimore, MD, pp.39–45.

Tomaseski-Heinemann, J. (1985) *Medical alert for persons with Prader–Willi syndrome*, Prader–Willi Syndrome Association, Edina, MN.

Tomaseski-Heinemann, J. (1988) A parent's point of view, in *Management of Prader–Willi syndrome* (eds L.R. Greenswag and R.C. Alexander), Springer-Verlag, NY, pp.182–94.

Turner, R. and Ruvalcaba, R.H. (1981) A retrospective study of the behavior of Prader–Willi syndrome versus other institutionalized retarded persons, in *Prader–Willi Syndrome* (eds V. A. Holm, S. J. Sulzbacher, and P. Pipes), Univ. Park Press, Baltimore, pp.215–18.

Tze, W.J., Dunn, H.G. and Rothstein, R.L. (1981) Endocrine profiles and metabolic aspects of Prader–Willi syndrome, in *Prader–Willi Syndrome* (eds. V. A. Holm, S. J. Sulzbacher, and P. Pipes), Univ. Park Press, Baltimore, pp. 281–91.

Umberger, F.G. (1984) Peabody Picture Vocabulary Test – Revised, in *Test Critiques: Vol. III* (eds D.J. Keyser and R.C. Sweetland), Test Corp. of America, Kansas City, pp.488–95.

United States Public Law 94–142, Education for all handicapped children act (1975) United States Code Service, The Lawyers Publishing, Rochester, NY.

Voshart, K., Groeneweg, G. and Baldwin, D. (1983) *Prader–Willi syndrome in Alberta: Prevalence and programs*, The Vocational and Rehabilitation Research Institute, Calgary.

Wannarachue, N., Ruvalcaba, R.H. and Kelly, V.C. (1975) Hypogonadism in Prader–Willi syndrome. *American J. of Mental Deficiency*, **79**(5), 592–603.

Warren, B. (1989) The hidden stage: Using drama to help teach the unspoken rules of social interaction, in *Learning Difficulties and Emotional Problems* (eds R.I. Brown and M. Chazan), Detselig, Calgary, AB.

Warren, J.L. and Hunt, E. (1981) Cognitive processing in children with Prader–Willi syndrome, in *Prader–Willi Syndrome* (eds V.A. Holm, S.J. Sulzbacher, and P. Pipes), Univ. Park Press, Baltimore, pp.161–77.

Watson, R.L. and Midlarsky, E. (1979) Reactions of mothers with mentally retarded children: A social perspective. *Psychological Reports*, **45**, 309–10.

Wett, M.A. (1988) A national parent network: The Prader–Willi Syndrome Association, in *Management of Prader–Willi Syndrome* (eds L.R. Greenswag and R.C. Alexander), Springer-Verlag, NY, pp.223–30.

Wett, R.J. (1985) Pain and symptoms. *The Gathered View*, **11**(2), 8.

Wilson, A.J. (1989) Ontario's Bill 82 in retrospect, in *Special education across Canada* (eds M. Csapo and L. Goguen), Centre for Human Development and Research, Vancouver, BC, pp.81–92.

Wilson, A., Cleal, T., Godsell, E. and Sheppard, W. (1989) The Special Education Policy of Newfoundland and Labrador, 1987: An analysis of its potential impact, in *Special Education Across Canada* (eds M. Csapo and L. Goguen), Centre for Human Development and Research, Vancouver, BC, pp. 133–47.

Winsor, E.J. and Welch, J.P. (1983) Prader–Willi syndrome associated with inversion of chromosome 15. *Clinical Genetics*, **24**, 456–61.

Wolfensberger, W. (1972) *Normalization: The principle of normalization in human services*, National Institute on Mental Retardation, Toronto.

Zellweger, H. (1969) The HHHO or Prader–Willi syndrome. *Birth defects: Original article series*, **5**(2), 15–17.

Zellweger, H. (1981) Diagnosis and therapy in the first phase of Prader–Willi syndrome, in *The Prader–Willi Syndrome* (eds V.A. Holm, S.J. Sulzbacher, and P. Pipes), Univ. Park Press, Baltimore, pp.55–68.

Zellweger, H. (1983) Prader–Willi syndrome abroad. *The Gathered View*, **9**(5), 4–5.

Zellweger, H. (1984) The Prader–Willi syndrome. *J. of the American Medical Association*, **25**(4), 18–35.

Zellweger, H. (1988) Differential diagnosis in Prader–Willi syndrome, in *Management of Prader–Willi Syndrome* (eds L.R. Greenswag and R.C. Alexander), Springer-Verlag, NY, pp.15–22.

Zellweger, H. and Schneider, H.J. (1968) Syndrome of hypotonia-hypomentia-hypogonadism-obesity (HHHO) or Prader–Willi syndrome. *American J. of Diseases of Children*, **115**, 588–98.

Zellweger, H. and Soper, R.T. (1979) The Prader–Willi syndrome, *Medicine & Hygiene*, **37**, 3338–45.

Zuffardi, O., Buhler, E.M. and Fraccaro, M. (1978) Chromosome 15 and Prader–Willi syndrome. *Clinical Genetics*, **14**, 315–16A.

# Author index

# Subject index